FLEXIBILITY

Other books by Paul McNaught-Davis

NCF Developing Flexibility (Resource Pack)
NCF Developing Flexibility (Teachers Pack)
You and Your Fitness and Health (Consultant Editor)
Food for Action (Contributor)
Sport Injury Clinic (Contributor)

FLEXIBILITY

How to Understand It

How to Achieve It

PAUL McNAUGHT-DAVIS

PARTRIDGE PRESS

LONDON · NEW YORK · TORONTO · SYDNEY · AUCKLAND

TRANSWORLD PUBLISHERS LTD
61–63 Uxbridge Road, London W5 5SA

TRANSWORLD PUBLISHERS (AUSTRALIA) PTY LTD
15–23 Helles Avenue, Moorebank, NSW 2170

TRANSWORLD PUBLISHERS (NZ) LTD
Cnr Moselle and Waipareira Aves,
Henderson, Auckland

Published 1991 by Partridge Press
a division of Transworld Publishers Ltd
Copyright © Paul McNaught-Davis 1991

A catalogue record for this title is available from the British
Library

ISBN 185225 1093

Printed in Great Britain
by Butler & Tanner, Frome, Somerset

With love to my wife, Jane,
my children, Adam, Beth, Anna and Jo(anne),
and my mum and dad.

ACKNOWLEDGEMENTS

The help I have received in the preparation of this book has been tremendous. Many folk helped in many ways and they are the real reason this book came about. So it is with many sincere thanks I acknowledge these debts of kindness.

Thanks are due,
. . . for all the encouragement and often practical help with reading, editing and amusing the children so that I could work, to my wife, Jane, and our close friends Graham, Myrene, Jo, Colin, Stella, Mark, Peter and Dawn;
. . . for all the work on researching the literature so thoroughly, to Simon Jenkins and Karen Hambly – both excellent ex-students of the BSc(Hons) Sport Science degree at Brighton Polytechnic;
. . . for being great subjects, to Sue Law, Steve Blake, Dawn Cook, Fiona Smith, Jane Wheeler, Chris Shambrook, Matthew Barker and Parambir Pahil, all staff, students or ex-students of the Chelsea School of Human Movement, Brighton Polytechnic;
. . . for photography, to George Deacon and graphics, to Richard Seymoor;
. . . for the excellent Foreword, to David Hemery;
. . . for real professional publishing help, to Debbie, Jennie and Dick;
. . . for the clothing used by all the main subjects in the photographs, NIKE (UK).

Finally a special thanks to the National Coaching Foundation and its hard working officers. This is not just for the permission to use some of their material in this text but also for getting me writing, back in 1984/5, on the Developing Flexibility course material for coaches.

CONTENTS

FOREWORD

Hurdlers, more than most performers, understand the value of flexibility work, and are painfully reminded with bruised knees if this is being neglected. Performers in most other sports do not have such harsh persuaders. That could be their misfortune. It has been my experience as a performer and coach, that flexibility has the double benefit of greatly reducing injury and also enhancing performance. Range of motion is a key attribute in speed, strength, skill, etc. One astonishing report came from a Toronto based football team who cut down their injury rate by 50 per cent in the season when they introduced a rigorous flexibility programme. The 1988 Olympic 400m hurdle winner, Debbie Flintoff-King, attributed her Olympic year improvement to her flexibility programme.

Flexibility work is too often seen by performers as a necessary evil, prior to the 'real' training. An alteration of perception is required. Flexibility should be 'part' of all health and fitness programmes. It is a beneficial life-long habit, up to and including the non sports playing elderly. I believe the mind, body and spirit are totally integrated. If this is true, could inflexibility of body be correlated with closed mindedness?

Flexibility is considered important enough in its own right to be one of the courses promoted by the National Coaching Foundation. The range of application of this book is extensive. It will be useful for performers and coaches looking for ways to achieve potential, at all personal levels. It may be used in planning beneficial and safe exercise programmes for fitness, health, recreation and rehabilitation. My experience is that the muscles shorten as a result of tears. Flexibility work is vital, to accompany the muscle rebuilding time, otherwise the shortened muscle will be MORE prone to future injury. And for the enquiring layman and student of sport and physical education the text provides understanding of the scientific basis of flexibility and stretching. As someone who, daily, is aiming to maintain flexibility I recommend this book to you.

David Hemery
1991

INTRODUCTION

Developing and maintaining flexibility remains the 'Cinderella' of modern training and performance in sport. Flexibility through stretching is being ignored by many, used ineffectively by others, and is causing damage to countless more who are being allowed to practise too aggressively.

There are many different reasons for flexibility training being a 'poor relation' in the sports training family. The most significant is that coaches and athletes have yet to be convinced of its importance, so naturally they place it low, if at all, on their priority lists. A contributing element in this 'willingness to ignore' flexibility work comes from the rather unfavourable comparison that stretching, as a procedure, makes with the dynamic training methods for skill, strength, speed and endurance.

Indeed these exciting qualities of skill, strength, speed and endurance are easy to identify in élite performance, but flexibility is not always so obvious and is therefore not perceived as an important element for good performance. Flexibility may even be seen as too dull to be as important as these other aspects of sport. The dullness is attributable, in part, to the slow and patient work necessary to achieve flexibility.

The training for flexibility should be, by its nature, quiet, painless, 'introverted', non-competitive and above all SLOW. Equally the expression of flexibility in sports performance is usually unobtrusive or masked by other elements such as strength. So flexibility training does little to push itself forward into the limelight.

In a few sports, like gymnastics, an excessive range of motion is the norm and flexibility training is a major part of any programme. The problem here is not ignoring flexibility in training but rather the safety and effectiveness of the methods used. Too often these procedures have been questionable and their application dangerous; this is especially worrying given the age profile of the performers in these sports. The need for extreme flexibility and the generally slow gains made by correct procedures have encouraged people to resort to dubious 'quick' methods. Some coaches are preparing children with fearsome disregard (through ignorance?) of the Pandora's box of injury they may be opening. This damage is happening now to countless dedicated youngsters although the manifestation of the damage as pain and disability may not become apparent until years later.

It is not that the knowledge of how to make things better and safer is unavailable, but just that the message seems to have failed to get across.

I have worked for quite some time now as a lecturer in the sports sciences and have not been blind to the slowness with which findings from my and related disciplines have penetrated the practice of sport. There is a need for better translation from the 'language' of the researcher to that of the coach or athlete.

There has been at least one positive move in recent years (in the UK) with the setting up of the National Coaching Foundation (NCF) in 1982/3 by the Sports Council.[1] This organization, some eight years on, is starting to make significant inroads into the problem of modernization and efficiency of coach education. (Any committed sports performer or coach wishing to improve their knowledge base would be well advised to contact the NCF (or its equivalent body outside this country) as this represents the best link, presently available, between the sport scientists and the performers.)

This book aims to help bridge the gap between theory and practice by making selected elements of sport science theory, concerning flexibility, available to a wider audience of sports people; and to make it available by making it practically applicable to sport.

Through these pages I hope to talk directly to those who have taken or are about to take up this exercise and sport commitment. In this I include not just the performers but also their coaches (and parents) who wish to improve standards and at the same time need or would like to know why particular strategies might help them and their athletes' performances and safety.

The text also aims to allow the reader to be able to use flexibility training as a major unifying factor so that the other aspects of training (strength, endurance, speed, skill etc.)

can be fully expressed as better performances.

Alongside the performance improving factors, yet just as important, flexibility training can help protect the body from much unnecessary injury and thus allow performers of all ages and standards to reach and sustain their individual optimum levels more consistently, safely and for longer.

There is a major thread in this text which explores the relationships between flexibility and injury in sport.

Flexibility training is relevant to all sports because it is about improving muscle performance through improving the range of active and passive motion. Hence flexibility can improve the quality of all other training and competition.

The text puts forward the best way to prepare as a sports performer (or just health seeker) so you can gain the benefits of exercise and avoid the disadvantages. This book is designed so you can select as much or as little of the training as you need or want according to your individual circumstances.

In summary the book is:

A manual of muscle stretching and care. At one level this text is simply an illustrated manual of what and how to stretch; providing a set of principles and practices related to the preparation of muscle for efficient work in whatever type of performance and at whatever level is being demanded. To this end there are specific recommendations applicable to different types of sport so that the reader can select the individual preparation required.

A rationale for activity leaders and providers. The book will be useful to those involved in the provision and promotion of exercise, at any standard or intensity, in their efforts to establish sensible practices which might improve the adherence (stickability) of newcomers to activity. Stretching and flexibility reduce muscle soreness and injury from sport which together form a major reason for presently high levels of drop out.

A resource for the student of sport science. Finally the text has a more academic side in that it explores the knowledge and research base for these techniques giving references and commentary useful to those wishing to know and understand rather than just being told what to do.

The true student (of sport and exercise) does not have the closed mind so typical of the worst in sport, but realizes that learning is a continuous process and that, at any moment in time, we are all just groping in the half-light for answers. The ability to look and look again at favoured practices, evaluate and analyse, make changes based on objective rather than subjective criteria and keep up with the relevant research and debate of your peers, are the real qualities of the professional (and committed amateur) in sport. This text, in its small way, may add to this debate which is at the root of evolving sport to a real professional status.[2]

[1]Sports Council, Annual Reports, 1982–3 (NCF decision September 1982), 1983–4 (NCF first report).
[2]McNaught-Davis, J. P., & McFee, G. Acreditation for a post-graduate profession in *Coach Education: Preparation for a Profession.* The proceedings of the VIII Commonwealth and International Conference on Sport, Physical Education, Dance, Recreation and Health. Glasgow 18–23 July 1986. London: Spon. 1986.

PART ONE

HE

THEORY OF

STRETCHING

FOR

FLEXIBILITY

1 WHY FLEXIBILITY TRAINING?

There is a tendency to talk and think of sports as if they were all similar but, of course, this is not so. They have many differences between them, not least in the demands they put on the human biological system; some are over quickly, some last for days, others require physical contact, while others are strictly non-contact, some need thirty or more to play together and yet others are individual in the extreme. However, although sports are all very different in terms of rules, time, skills, etc., there are ways of classifying them into groups on physiological grounds.

Although few sports are absolutely pure in terms of their particular physiological demands, exercise scientists tend to classify sports into three types: the endurance (stamina) sports; the power (strength and speed) sports; and, sports where endurance and power are combined more or less equally.

Endurance type exercise – i.e. low (submaximal) intensity and long duration – is recognized as having the most health benefits in terms of physiologically conditioning the heart, lungs and circulation. Within this group are cycling, jogging, swimming, hiking, cross country skiing or orienteering type sports.

Sports where endurance plays a major part but power is also crucial for sprints or maximum exertions within the game, are those like soccer, hockey, netball, ice hockey and rugby. These 'mixed' sports may be mixed in that all the players need a bit of endurance and a bit of power. On the other hand they may require some players to be completely, or almost completely, one or the other. A goalminder in ice hockey is a power athlete whereas the other players are much more committed to endurance.

The non-endurance or 'sprint' type activity, like weight lifting, sprint running and swimming, golf (hitting the ball) and throwing events, tend to increase strength and explosive power but seem to have less obvious health benefits. They are a lot healthier than doing nothing, of course, but do not rely on the cardiovascular (heart and lungs) fitness of the endurance sports. Strength and speed are very important aspects of training in most sports, even when the emphasis may be on endurance.

From korfball to karate and synchronized swimming to ultimate, all sports are distinct and their appeal is equally varied. It may be that there is only one real commonality between sports and that is that the performance quality achieved is related to the quality of training undertaken.

The quality of training in many sports has suffered from an overriding concentration by coaches and players on the parts (strengths, endurance, speed, skill, etc.) without sufficient attention being given to the process of unifying them into the whole.

The practice game and performance are seen as places and times where the trained parts are traditionally brought together, which is important in order that the individuals can learn to express their skills effectively. However, at a more fundamental level prior to practice games and competition there should be another ongoing stage, a kind of internal, physiological equivalent to the practice game.

This mechanism is the one by which the neuro-muscular (nerve impulses and muscle actions) qualities built up through training are 'taught' to act with empathy, so that through co-ordinated expression the whole becomes much more than the sum of its parts. Flexibility training is such a fundamental mechanism and unifying process.

Flexibility training is much more than just a process for increasing ranges of motion. It also prepares the muscular system for quality action. You may be able to increase the range by any old inappropriate stretching, but with correct stretching you can gain so much more.

Flexibility is one of only two elements of sports fitness which have yet to be taken seriously by the majority of sports performers. The other is the training of mental skills which, as we will see, has much more in common with flexibility than just the fact it too is being ignored by large sections of the sporting world.

The well-exercised individual should be able to cope better with the stresses and strains of everyday life, both physiologically and psychologically.

Psychological benefits are also supposed to accrue from the reduction of stress, improved self-image and confidence which are associated with improved fitness through exercise. Whether or not this type of psychological health is more associated with one or other type of sport or is totally dependent on the individual, mental health is at least as important as any other form of health.

Certainly this type of reasoning is behind the efforts made by the various groups in the 'health through exercise lobby'. It is naturally seen as crucial that a special effort should be placed on getting a higher level of commitment from young people in an attempt to lay the foundations for a lifelong participation in sport.

In recent years, we have been exposed to increasing exercise propaganda, through what we watch on TV and listen to on radio, what we read in our newspapers and magazines and what is officially sanctioned via various 'government agency' initiatives. Books on workouts, aerobics, jogging and weight training appear in nearly every shop and media advertising exploits the beautiful muscular body; the sport we see on TV emphasizes the high-level (élite) performer and encourages everyone, especially our children, to emulate their success. The 'carrot' offered to the potential new recruit, either directly, or more often, by association, is the (supposed) health spin-off as much as any enjoyment the activity might bring. Sport For All and other such projects all educate us towards an active and healthy lifestyle. There can be only a few ostriches left unaware of the established and establishment view: exercise is good for us.

The health aspect of exercise is considered an important justification for pushing sport for everyone, but how much does this really help recruitment

and adherence to sport? The vast majority who play games and sports do so for other reasons than just health – they may like sport for its own sake; they may be fascinated by the strategies of training and skill which underpin all great performances; they may want to get better at their chosen sport for the satisfaction that that brings with it. They are often prepared to work long and hard at getting better whatever the reasons they may have for doing it.

If sports promoters (parents, coaches, physical education teachers and health promotion officers) adopted the principles contained in these pages then they would have better success than they presently do in gaining and keeping recruits to sport and exercise.

The thrust of this book is directed at the committed sports performer, coach, sports parent and the 'student' of sports science, but it is also important to consider the reasons why people do not exercise as the best promoters of sport *can be* those involved. Flexibility training can be an important asset in bringing people into sport.

WHY WE DO NOT EXERCISE

Despite the overwhelming campaign to encourage people to participate in sport, only about 25 per cent of the population take regular exercise. Why do we resist? Are we a nation of unbelievers despite the avalanche of evidence? Don't we care about living long and well? Does 75 per cent of the population have severe psychological problems making them resist all things that are good for them?

Although some people still do active jobs these are much rarer now; even around the home tasks are physically less demanding – few have fires to rake out or logs to cut and carry in; vacuum cleaners have replaced carpet beating, dish washers are taking over from washing up by hand, and who pushes a lawn mower nowadays?

There is little doubt that on the whole we do not do enough 'huffing and puffing' as part of our daily work, but we seem to resist it in our leisure time too! As Per-O Astrand explains in discussing Kalihari bushmen, exercise is not a primitive drive like the need for food. These bushmen and women walk fast for many hours a day to gather enough food to live on. They do not jog, they *are* well trained, but they do not do this exercise for its own sake. The reason is hunger.

Modern reasons to do exercise never include freedom from hunger; and promised longevity may be a bit too abstract for the young or even the middle-aged. If sport can really be fun and painless (or mostly painless) perhaps it will be able to compete better with the other draws on our leisure time. This has an obvious health education context but also, think of the increase in potential for the standards of sport. For example, the UK cannot compete internationally at tennis with a country like Sweden (population about one seventh of the UK), but if UK tennis could, say, treble its 'membership' and then keep them, think of the added potential!

This book cannot promise the revitalization of British tennis but it can help make those that try a sport more likely to stay by easing the physical trauma and increasing the potential for improving the standards reached.

The lack of support for a healthy, activity-based lifestyle is rather complex and is related to combinations of reasons for different people:

ACTIVE JOBS

Some people will be doing a lot of activity as part of their jobs and rightly feel they are getting many of the expected health benefits already. They may want, therefore, to rest and relax away from work. If sports can be seen as good ways to relax, even for those who are active as part of their work, then again sports can expect to benefit in recruitment.

For those with physically demanding occupations, flexibility work would help them sustain their level of work and assist the recovery between bouts of hard work, just as it does in sport.

PRESSURE OF WORK AND WORKPLACE EXERCISE

Others may find that work has to come first and having travelled home there is no time for going out to sport centres etc. without missing out on family life. Workplace-based opportunities to be active have been shown to be profit enhancing to the companies involved. Predominantly this research is from the USA as there is still resistance to, or ignorance of, its introduction in a lot of other countries. The clear argument and evidence suggest that the allocation of time to workplace activity opportunities improves productivity, reduces absenteeism and pays for itself. Flexibility training should be part of that programme so that people are less likely to suffer injuries or experience pain as a result of their activity. Adherence to new exercise programmes could then be expected to improve and drop-out rates to reduce.

FACILITIES AND FINANCE

For many the most important reason for not participating in sport is the lack of appropriate facilities catering for family groups at an affordable price. Flexibility training is free from all financial considerations as it requires no apparatus, no special clothing and no one else.

SCHOOL-DAY EXPERIENCES

Many of us may have been put off sport at school by cold, wet afternoons stood shivering in goal or on the wing while all the play took place a hundred yards away. Others remembering their school-days will know they were 'turned off' by the emphasis on élite performance and the lack of encouragement given to the less naturally talented. For all these people exercise is synonymous with discomfort, humiliation and boredom.

Sports in general and teachers in particular have to dispel this notion and modern PE teachers do seem to be getting to grips with this. An approach which includes better preparation of the muscles for these activities must help the fight, as it reduces soreness and injury and increases self-control and potential for performance.

MAKE THE FIRST MOVE!

If you have the money, the time and the facilities and have managed to get through your youth without being taught by an overbearing, narrow-minded, élitist, sadist – why don't you do some exercise?

This is where those involved in sport become their own worst enemies. Sports do not always make recruitment easy for the 'newcomer'. Here are a few examples:

EXPOSURE – VANITY – POSERS

A typical degradation is that you have to take most of your clothes off and expose your carefully cultivated white whale-blubber to the critical, even judgemental, eyes of the seemingly endless rows of long-legged, tanned, 'anorexic' looking Jane Fonda clones or equally numerous and bronzed but muscular, possibly brain dead, 'macho' posers which seem to adorn all our gyms and sport centres. Or, at least, this is what the paranoia tells the potential recruit – not how good it is for him or her to be active or how most people are just as incompetent and nervous as they are.

If, plucking up their courage, they overcome these carefully cultivated paranoid feelings about their UGLY BODY and practical incompetences, and, for example, sink quietly into the corner of a swimming pool, there are other trials to endure. As they stand there, hoping the liquid blurs the edges of their shameful outline, they are splashed by hooligan children or quickly get blinded by the neat chlorine in which they are trying to exercise. The converted could sometimes be more aware and sympathetic towards the traumas of starting up a new activity. Flexibility training can help such an easy introduction.

UNACCUSTOMED EXERCISE HURTS

Joining say a badminton club might be an alternative activity to swimming but it too can have its problems. This type of sport often entails having to compete immediately and, being new, you tend to lose which in turn may mean you play less. The 'winner stays on' mentality may not now be so common away from the pool table, but if it is present, in any form, it can be a crucial 'turn off' for the newcomer. Practise with better players if you can, but compete, at least to start with, with others of like standards and aspirations.

So, returning to the newcomer at the club, he probably tries harder to win, but still loses and begins to become tense and fretful about an activity which should have been enjoyable.

If he does manage to get plenty of play at the start, he will probably put in a lot of effort and, at best, feel sick and, at worse, be sick. Then the next day he is unable to walk and feels as if, in the night, someone has injected his muscles with a mixture of lead and razor blades which is fine as long as he doesn't want to breathe or move.

None of this needs to be part of sport. Flexibility training is the best antidote to the ravages of exercise.

SKILL AND INJURY
During the earliest days of a new flirtation with sport, skill and fitness levels are at their lowest and the chances of accidental injury are highest. When combined with an enthusiasm pushing the participant along without any common-sense thought to how fit or skilled they actually are, injury often results leading the newcomer to believe that they had been wrong to start; and so they give up, and a few more people slide away from sport. If more of the early periods of introduction were spent on preparation for, rather than actual fullblooded, activity this loss to sport could be reduced.

CHILDREN'S ACTIVITY LEVELS
There are often better facilities and certainly better trained teachers available to our children than there were twenty to thirty years ago, but there is hardly any money to support the system. Increasingly a very dissatisfied staff are less able or willing to improve the real opportunities for children, and things could get even worse before they get better.

Current research into the health of children indicates that large numbers of school-age children are rarely raising their heart rates through exercise at school or home. The following is from the abstract of a paper given in 1989 at the 14th seminar on Pediatric Work Physiology at Leuven, Belgium, by Neil Armstrong:

In the ten-year-old children . . . 18 per cent of the boys and 22 per cent of the girls failed to elicit a single 10 minute period with their heart rate above 140 bts/min. The thirteen-year-old girls displayed significantly lower heart rates than the boys and spent significantly fewer sustained 5 or 10 minute periods with heart rates above 70 per cent of maximum. 50 per cent of the girls and 21 per cent of the boys never achieved a single 10 minute period with their heart rate above 140 bts/min.

Yet it is generally hoped that patterns of behaviour set at school will influence the future lifestyle of the adult. Things therefore look a little bleak.

MICRO-CHIP ALTERNATIVES
Children have, as we all do, many colourful, easy, immediately gratifying, warm and sedentary leisure alternatives based around the plastics and micro-chip revolutions. So sport is up against tough competition for their time.

POORLY EDUCATED COACHES AND DAMAGED CHILDREN

Historically, sport has been run predominantly by well-meaning amateurs. The lack of coach education has meant that we often see sports coaches being shamefully wasteful of even the keenest of our sporting youth, who, by some chance, are motivated to try sport and exercise. The coaches tend to do this by the lack of care they take of growing bodies and the emphasis they put on strength, speed, endurance and winning rather than enjoyment. The National Coaching Foundation is making the right noises and has produced a start towards making sports coaching more professional. This is a desperately important initiative which should not be seen to suffer through lack of money, or the inertia of sporting establishments.

POOR ORGANIZATION OF SPORTING EVENTS

Even at tournament competitions keen youngsters can be made to wait around becoming bored and disillusioned with the idea of exercise for fun. A specific example of this happened to my teenage son at a recent badminton competition:

Sunday morning, leaving home at eight o'clock, drive thirty miles, report in to tournament table. No heating in the hall but children forbidden to play in tracksuits. Wait for two hours. First game – beaten. Wait for two hours to play game in plate competition – win. Wait for one hour for second game in plate – beaten. Entered doubles without partner. Although a partner is available, wait an hour for a decision. Told cannot play because the sheet is already prepared. Go home. Arrive home at seven o'clock.

This competition was organized by nationally qualified officials and yet it broke nearly every rule of common sense, physiology and psychology, and succeeded in putting one more nail in the exercise coffin for a number of previously well-motivated kids.

This scenario is not by any means the preserve of badminton – similar things can be seen in many sports. Many of these officials/adults should be asking themselves if their list of priorities is really correct. Reducing the players by half after the first set of matches instead of using round robins seems an inappropriate strategy, if encouraging more young people to play is the *real* aim. Equally silly is the practice of holding to outdated and pointless standards of dress and increasing the risk of injury. If, in the example, one of the three officials had been designated to organize a proper warm up and gentle stretching exercises (in tracksuits), the other two would have been less bothered by competitors around the tournament table. Instead, one official was constantly stopping children from warming up and telling the players to take off their tracksuits. Quite funny, if it wasn't so sad.

WHAT FLEXIBILITY TRAINING CAN DO

There is another way that can make exercise different from any of the horrors above. Exercise can be painless and fun and healthy all at the same time. Sport can be of the highest quality without being necessarily painful and fraught with injury. Exercise does not have to be stressful or embarrassing. And, most of all, you can prepare your body slowly and specifically, at any age, for an appropriate sport or just to gain the benefits (while avoiding the ills) of activity. Flexibility training as the process of preparation has many of the health benefits of exercise with none of the risks and actually makes exercise really available to all.

Clearly many people have neither the wish nor the time to play sport very regularly. For them, however, the maintenance of their independence to do the things they want to do will become important as they grow older. To walk up stairs and dress themselves and do the shopping are activities which maintain the fabric of their independent lives. These everyday activities progressively become more demanding and even more dangerous if the range of muscle function is allowed to become restricted. The progress of this ageing process will be related to inherited characteristics as well as the accumulation of environmental influences; there will be much variety from person to person but by using stretching exercises regularly many ageing effects can be offset. What is more, all the simple care of muscle tissue can be achieved at home, with no fancy equipment, not even a tracksuit.

You can even use the time spent doing normal everyday activities like reading the paper, taking a bath and washing up. This point should be a real fillip for the sports performer with his overcommitted lifestyle. Just think of it . . . training in bed!

People should be encouraged to play sport at every opportunity and at the highest standard they can safely play it. However, some people who promote exercise do not always do a great job, because they tend to make few distinctions between types of exercise or different aspirations in terms of standard. Elitism abounds and is not for everyone. To avoid this problem, we need to emphasize from the start the idea of individual differences, needs and aspirations. Clearly we are all very different and our training programmes should be individually tailored to fit and not just taken off the shelf having one size, colour and style, like army uniforms.

The worst offenders are often quality ex-sportsmen who lack a realistic concept of how hard some people find the skills of sport. Or they may be 'zealots with a mission', trying to make you feel guilty because you are not running twenty miles a week or spending every evening in the gym.

If there is an underlying philosophy to this text it is that flexibility training, as a full and integrated part of sport, would improve standards, decrease wastage and improve the long-term health of participants.

Flexibility training is the best way to prepare for exercise, be it as a sports performer or as a health seeker, to gain the benefits without the disadvantages. And you can select as much or as little as you need or want according to your individual circumstances.

WHAT IS EXERCISE ANYWAY?

It is important not to have a restricted concept of activity and exercise and, if you have, to recognize now that the term should include *anything* which includes an increase in energy output. So, for the habitually sedentary, walking regularly down to the shops and back is exercise and would produce similar training effects as running or cycling miles would for the fitter person. There are many alternatives to the traditional team games and sports, including window shopping, beachcombing, gardening, cleaning the oven, walking in the swimming pool, french cricket, making love at different speeds, window cleaning, shopping on foot, non-competitive squash, washing the car more often than usual, korfball, mini-tennis, painting the house, etc., etc., etc.

The preparation of muscles for any form of exercise should be basically the same. This preparation, through stretching, will be for some unfit individuals nearly an exercise in itself, because just getting into position to stretch will raise the energy output above sedentary levels. At the other extreme of fitness it will be the maintenance of muscle condition for top performance and be combined with other forms of training to achieve this end.

STRETCHING TECHNIQUE

Muscles work the body and it must be the conditioning of these muscles which is the main concern from now on. Although the emphasis in the text will be on conditioning through stretching it will not be taken in isolation from the other important and interrelated aspects of training. However, the central topic concerns the use of stretching as a means towards the end of safe and effective activity, be that at Olympic or normal levels.

As mentioned earlier, flexibility has been generally given short measure (at best) by coaches and athletes and ignored (at worst) by many sports performers.

Among those that pay lip service to flexibility training it has often been consigned to either 'a warm-up stretch' or 'some quick bounces' or 'a bit of both'. Certainly it would not rate alongside strength or endurance as a significant percentage of training time. This state of affairs needs to change and this book aims to persuade the doubters.

At the other extreme there are the confirmed 'flexibility seekers'; but too often these groups are gaining a range of motion at the cost of long-term physical damage and, at the same time, are failing to express their strength, speed or endurance optimally. They either do not know the correct theory and practice or do not choose to use it. This text addresses these problems.

REFERENCES

Armstrong, N., Balding, J., Bray, S., Gentle, P. and Kirby, B., 'The Physical Activity Patterns of 10 and 13 Year Old Children', paper given at 14th International Seminar on Pediatric Work Physiology, Leuven, Belgium, 1989

Astrand, P-O, *Health and Fitness*, Skandia Insurance Company Ltd, Stockholm, 1978

McNaught-Davis, J. P. and McFee, G., 'Acreditation for a post-graduate profession', in *Coach Education: Preparation for a Profession*, the proceedings of the VIII Commonwealth and International Conference on Sport, Physical Education, Dance, Recreation and Health. Glasgow 18–23 July 1986. London: Spon. 1986

McNaught-Davis, J.P., 'Health-related Fitness vs. Health-related Leisure', from *Leisure, Labour and Lifestyles: International comparisons,* Vol II: *Leisure and the Quality of Life: Themes and Issues,* edited by Tomlinson, A. LSA Conference papers No 42, pp67–73, 1990

Sports Council, Annual Reports, 1978–9 (Sport for All), 1982–3 (NCF decision September 1982), 1983–4 (NCF first report)

The Sports Council's National Seminar and Exhibition, Recreation management 1988, *Working out . . . at work,* Workshop Report, 22–24 March 1988

2

YOUR ANATOMICAL LIMITS

A door hinge has a range of motion through which it will normally swing with ease. There are lots of different hinges with lots of different ranges of normal motion designed for a variety of similar but different jobs, but all classified as hinges.

No one is surprised if, when one of these hinges is forced open beyond its limit, damage is done. The damage may be directly to the metal hinge, its securing screws or the wood attached. After the damage has occurred the hinge does not function as a new hinge would; permanent changes are apparent.

Another hinge, this time on a seldom used door, will eventually start to lose its functional capacity as dust and rust increase the friction between surfaces and closely aligned but separate contours become semi-fused together. Yet another door with fairly constant use through only a limited angle, due to some permanent obstruction or other, will begin to lose mobility through the unused portion of the potential range, while maintaining function in the used portion.

The correctly used and regularly oiled hinge, and the hinge allowed to work in the most suitable environment, will do a good job. But the hinge that has the right design features for the job and is then treated right will out-perform the rest.

As with the realities of this simple mechanical engineering analogy, the treatment dealt out to the human machine over the years is crucial to its efficiency. However, the best or worst of treatment can not fundamentally change limitations inherent in the design features. Change that occurs at the structural level (like the over-stretched hinge) may give an actual increase in range but at the permanent cost of the loss of another function or two (for the door, security).

It is impossible to appreciate the reasoning behind flexibility training strategies or to understand the mechanisms of tissue damage related to injury through training, without a grasp of human design.

This chapter introduces a very selective pot-pourri of anatomical information chosen to illustrate and illuminate the limitations imposed on training effectiveness by the nature and arrangement of human tissues. Without this background it is not possible to have a clear appreciation of the range of individual, human capacities relevant to movement and movement potential. For all coaches, therefore, there is a professional and, in my view, morale responsibility to learn about these and other fundamentals of applied biology before they impose training regimes on their athletes. For the athlete (or young athlete's parent) by knowing this background they can confidently question the wisdom of a coach's

demands on themselves (or their sporty offspring). The coach who cannot explain satisfactorily the theoretical basis of their training programmes must be considered a potential hazard.

In this first section, then, it is the structural elements as revealed through the study of anatomy that are investigated. Subsequently other fundamentals more to do with functional considerations of physiology and growth and development are explored.

This factual material has significant health and injury implications which are often overlooked or ignored in the pursuit of excellence. Many of the limitations to our range of motion comes from our personal set of inherited characteristics (genes) more than the extent and quality of our training. Indeed, it is fair to say much of the traumatization of tissue associated with training and playing sport comes from an ignorance or denial of these 'inbuilt' limitations.

It seems most appropriate to start with some of the structures on which movement is based because understanding basic anatomy helps put the process of improvement through training in a realistic context. Although people may recognize that the standards of sport performances will be more than the sum of the individual trained aspects, it is unlikely that many will see anatomical features as inflicting serious limitations on the outcome.

These limitations are of two types. They can be of the kind which may be ignored but at the significant risk of inflicting either short- or long-term injury. Or, they may be the kind which place specific performance restrictions on individuals which, to an extent, inevitably define their improvement potential and/ or their choice of technique in a given sport.

The basic premise of flexibility training is that it can unlock the full potential of any individual's performance at least in terms of the range of motion. It should be appreciated, however, that it cannot 'put in what God left out' and any training quest to modify those aspects of an individual's anatomy which are by definition 'unmodifiable' are doomed. It is hoped that this section sets the margins of the changeable and the non-changeable and gives a clear rationale for the use of specific flexibility training methods based on this knowledge.

THE JOINTS

A joint is the structure where two or more bones meet. Our joints make it possible for our muscles to move our bones. However, not all joints are designed to move or to allow movement.

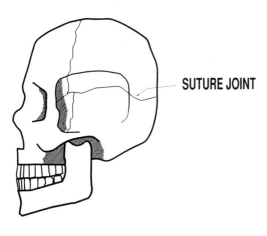

DIAGRAMATIC SKULL SHOWING SUTURE JOINT

Three types of joints can be distinguished: *Joints which do not permit movement* – where adjacent bones are united by a thin layer of dense fibrous tissue, for example, the suture joints of the skull. The joint here allows the growing process to finish with a complete protection around the brain.

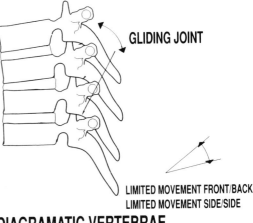

DIAGRAMATIC VERTEBRAE GLIDING JOINT

Joints which permit some movement – like those between the bodies of the spinal vertebrae, where bones are held together with a thick layer of fibrous tissue of fibre-cartilage. If a full range of motion was possible at these joints, vital structures associated with the nervous system which run nearby could be endangered.

Joints with freedom of movement – these are commonly known as synovial joints. They consist of a cavity enclosed by a capsule of fibrous tissue similar to ligaments and often associated with ligaments which reinforce the capsule. The ends of the bones are covered with articular cartilage – known as hyaline cartilage. (Next time you prepare a roast dinner, look inside one of the 'joints' and you will see a silvery glistening area covering the articulating surfaces – this is a hyaline.) The capsule is lined with synovial membrane which secretes a lubricant called synovial fluid. Hence the articular cartilage provides a smooth, sliding surface for bones.

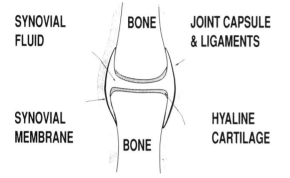

SYNOVIAL FLUID — BONE — JOINT CAPSULE & LIGAMENTS

SYNOVIAL MEMBRANE — BONE — HYALINE CARTILAGE

SECTION THROUGH A SIMPLE SYNOVIAL JOINT

The shape, size and direction of the articular surfaces determine the degree of movement, the type of movement and, the plane in which the movement takes place. Although the basic knee or elbow

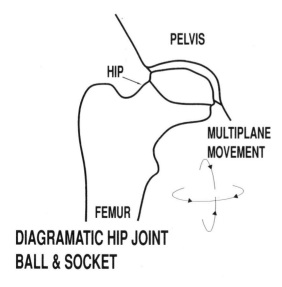

PELVIS

HIP

MULTIPLANE MOVEMENT

FEMUR

DIAGRAMATIC HIP JOINT BALL & SOCKET

structure is the same from person to person, there are many subtle differences which can make significant contributions to the actual movement potential of an individual joint.

There are a variety of synovial joint types which can be classified into six groups according to the type of basic shape and thus movement:

BALL AND SOCKET JOINT

This is where a rounded head of one bone fits into the concave cavity of another. This type of joint provides the widest range of motion, including rotation. An example is the shoulder joint between the head of the humerus (ball) and the glenoid fossa of the scapula (socket).

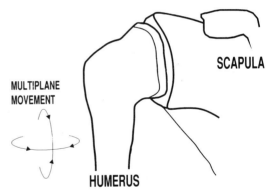

MULTIPLANE MOVEMENT

SCAPULA

HUMERUS

DIAGRAMATIC SHOULDER JOINT BALL & SOCKET

HINGE JOINT

This is where the convex surface of one bone fits a concave surface of another in such a way that motion is limited to extension and flexion, for example, the elbow.

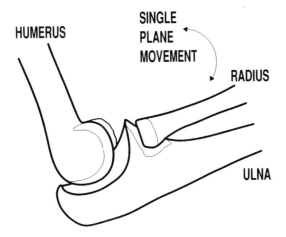

DIAGRAMATIC ELBOW JOINT HINGE

PIVOT JOINT

This joint is formed by a pivot-like process within a fossa (hole) of another bone. Motion is limited to rotation, for example, atlas/axis; these are the two upper bones of the vertebral column which together allow for the head movement of rotation.

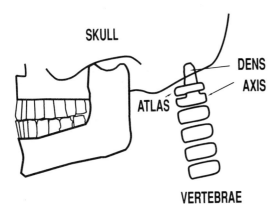

DIAGRAMATIC NECK JOINT PIVOT

CONDYLOID JOINT

This is where an oval-shaped condyle fits into an elliptical cavity. The movements of flexion, extension, abduction (away from the mid-line) and adduction (towards the mid-line) are possible. Adding these movements together gives circumduction as can be seen in the hand where the metacarpal/phalangeal joints occur in the fingers and the palm.

SADDLE JOINT

This is a unique joint found only in the thumb. The articular surface is concave in one direction and convex in the other; the opposing articular surfaces are reciprocally convex/concave so that the bones fit together. Movements are similar to that of the condyloid joint but rather freer. In evolutionary terms the opposition of the fingers by the thumb has been described as a very significant step. The mutual development of brain and hand in terms of intricate manipulative skills would seem to have been impossible but for this joint arrangement.

GLIDING JOINT

This is formed by the opposing plane surfaces of slightly convex and concave surfaces permitting gliding movement only; for example, transverse processes of vertebrae. See diagram on p.14: Diagrammatic Vertebrae Gliding Joint.

The greater the range and variety of movement allowed by the structure of a joint, then the more potentially unstable is that joint. If a joint become unstable at any point in its travel there is an immediate increase in the risk of injury. The injury may be to the joint itself, the associated tissue or to some remote part as a consequence of trying to correct for the instability and/or failing to make that correction.

The stability of joints is thus fundamental to maintaining the health of both that joint and the tissues associated with it. The crucial factors for the maintenance of stability can be identified and need to be considered in relation to how one trains and performs.

Stability of joints is determined by:

Ligaments associated with the joint in question. Ligaments limit movement in specific directions determined by their position. (The ligaments are considered in more detail later in this section.)

Muscle tension. The stronger the muscles whose tendons pass over a joint, the greater the joint's stability as long as that strength is equally balanced, i.e. one muscle does not pull more than another. With respect to the immature skeleton this strength should be developed very carefully as 'overstrong' muscles in the young body can disrupt bone growth areas. This developmental point is seen as a crucial element in the arguments for and against élite performance for young children and is pursued in Chapter 4.

The properties of the deep fascia. This refers to the non-contractile supportive tissue associated with the contractile elements of muscle. The contracting fibres are held in place and the forces which they generate are transmitted via this tissue. Damage to the fascia tissue can be just as debilitating as damage to the active muscle fibres. (Fascia tissue is reviewed separately later in this section.)

Atmospheric pressure and capillary action. Perhaps rather surprisingly, this is important. The pressure within articular cavities is lower than atmospheric pressure and this serves to hold the bones together, as the evacuation of the gases in the joints has the same effect as pushing a rubber sucker onto a wall. This is aided by the small amount of synovial fluid present in most joints, which gives a cohesion similar to a drop of water between two pieces of glass, which, lubricated by only a minimum of the fluid, slide over each other very easily but are much more difficult to pull apart than they would have been without the fluid. These two adhesive qualities are important stability devices which work best in the closely packed joint. If through use or trauma these surfaces become less adjacent then this adhesion is less effective, stability is compromised, and recurring injury becomes more likely. The effective range of motion may also be increased, but without being able to impose proper control.

The shape of the bone structure. For example, the deep socket at the hip joint gives greater stability than does the shallow socket at the shoulder joint.

The stability of the joint has to be considered alongside the range of motion of that joint because the two are inextricably connected through the dynamics of motion. A joint at one point in its possible range may be stable enough, but as it moves towards the limit of the range then stability may be considerably less.

The range of motion in a joint is dependent on:

Bone structure. For example, the ball and socket joint of the shoulder with its shallow socket, permits a greater variety and range of movements than, say the hinge-type arrangement of the elbow joint. (See diagrams on p.15.)

The properties of the soft tissue near the joint. In particular the joint capsule and ligaments – long or short fibres with more or less elasticity will change the potential range for that joint. The elasticity of muscles, fascia and tendons will impose more or less resistance to motion. The quantity of scar tissue, fat deposits and so on, can all add to the total picture and the apparent or actual range of motion available and the individual differences seen between joints in the same body and from one person to another.

The range of motion is in fact a combination of these aspects plus the added effects of many joints together; for example, shoulder flexibility is increased by the combined action of the joints of the shoulder girdle, as in the butterfly swimming stroke.

Many of these anatomical attributes are set in the individual by their genetic make-up and changing them to improve flexibility would cause actual damage. For example, a bone shape cannot be modified without damage. Likewise the thickness of a vertebral disc is set and gives an inherited limit to some spinal movements. If you are born with comparatively thick intervertebral discs then when you hyperextend your back (see diagram below) there is the potential for more squeezing and thus more hyperextension than for the individual with a thin set of discs. Other factors like muscle tightness may be stopping the fullest employment of this characteristic so much that the person with the thin discs has a better actual range of motion. However, training could reverse this. The thin discs cannot be modified and have a limit beyond the capacity of training to alter. The worry is that not recognizing this limit might encourage attempts to increase the range in such a way that bone meets bone and damage takes place. Training should not be aimed at modification of the set genetic patterns but at getting the most from them. Ideally, the training method adopted reduces, by its nature, any chance of any type of damage.

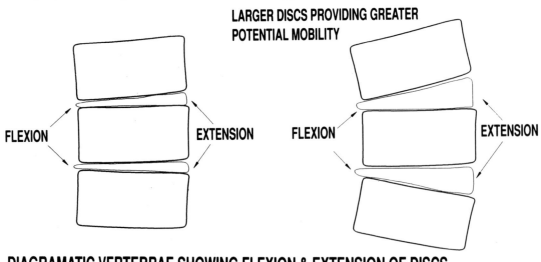

LARGER DISCS PROVIDING GREATER POTENTIAL MOBILITY

FLEXION   EXTENSION   FLEXION   EXTENSION

DIAGRAMATIC VERTEBRAE SHOWING FLEXION & EXTENSION OF DISCS

CONNECTIVE TISSUE

A large group of tissues comes under the title of connective tissue due to their common function connecting and supporting the other tissues. Fascia, ligaments, joint capsules, cartilage, tendons (including aponeuroses) are all different forms of connective tissues which are important to movement.

FASCIA

The skin is separated from the muscles and bones by two layers of fibrous tissue, the superficial fascia and the deep fascia, which are connective tissues of varying thickness and density depending on the part of the body in which they are found. Superficial fascia is a fat-filled fibrous mesh that connects the skin to the underlying sheet of deep fascia. Deep fascia is dense, elastic tissue that sheathes the muscles and the vessels and nerves which lie between them. When you stretch, this tissue will stretch but eventually it will be resistant to movement.

LIGAMENTS

Ligaments are strong bands of tissue with limited elasticity. They consist of fibrous, connective tissue which connects bones, especially at the joints. Ligaments tend to bind bones closely together while allowing a limited range of movement in a given direction. They are extra strong where stress and strain are most likely to occur, thus protecting the joint from damage. Ligaments are designed to limit movement.

Overstretching ligaments can permanently reduce their effectiveness.

Any suspected ligament damage must be followed up with a full medical investigation because damage to ligaments during youth may only become apparent as a chronic problem many years later. The stability of joints relies in part on muscle strength and tension which diminishes with the passing of the years. As the muscles weaken and cannot assist the ligaments so well then the ligaments become the only significant support. However, if maybe ten or twenty years previously these ligaments were permanently damaged by overstretching them then the support they can give is much less. For example, the spinal joints may slide too much trapping little nerves, and causing pain and distress – it does seem that the back is particularly susceptible. Many gymnasts and dancers will testify to chronic back problems years after they stop competition.

Thus the anatomy gives us a clear rule: no stretching training should include the stretching of ligaments beyond their normal range and, specifically, stretching training should not be aimed at improvements through overstretching ligaments.

When not being put under any strain the outline of the ligament fibres are wavy and as they take up any applied tension this outline is pulled out to a straight line increasingly resisting the movement causing the strain; and thus supporting the joint through its proper movement. If the ligament is then allowed to return to its resting tension the original outline is restored. This is all 'the normal and correct' functioning of ligaments. Overstressing the ligaments beyond their straight outline especially on a continuous basis through, say, hyperextension exercises of the wrong sort, will damage the tissue. This will be seen as an inability to regain their wavy outline and consequently a permanent inability to grip the joint properly. The joint loses stability and gains a less controllable but additional range of motion. This is not a true increase in flexibility although it is often thought to be so. This is a pathological increase in motion and should be avoided. The improved range of motion so gained leaves the joint less stable and susceptible to damage. How many sports performers do you know with recurring ankle twists for example? Although usually this is initially caused by one traumatic over-stretching of the ligaments, it is the same type of ligament damage caused by bad flexibility work and the same permanant instability often occurs.

By the nature of chronic damage, when it becomes noticeable the aetiology (causation) may be difficult to pinpoint and research on such damage is very difficult. Nevertheless, the overwhelming majority of sports medical literature and professional comment seems to be convinced that long-term abuse of ligaments through over-stretching is a major contributer to chronic pain in sports performers and ex-sports performers.

JOINT CAPSULES

The ligamentous sleeve that envelops the two bone ends of a joint is called the joint capsule. The capsule is reinforced by ligaments, but again, and in the same way as described above, overstretching can cause weakness and in the long term, unstable and painful joints. Different joints tend to have varying degrees of laxity in the capsule and this also varies between individuals. (*See also* hyper and hypo mobility.)

CARTILAGE

Cartilage is a dense, hard tissue, comparable in its toughness to bone but, unlike bone, much more flexible and resilient.

Hyaline-articular cartilage covers the articular surfaces of bones and maintains a smooth surface during movement of one bone on another. The circulation of nutrients to this cartilage relies on movement in the joint; so a restrictive regime of joint movement can contribute to the deterioration of the tissue. Also the cartilage has no feeling and therefore can be damaged without causing pain and without you knowing it. Inappropriate activities in youth can damage cartilage, the damage not being apparent until it is too late. Maybe ten or twenty years later the 'errors of your ways' come home as your backache or knee pains become a continuous reminder. Correct procedures are vital in reducing long-term chronic injury. Eventually the injury may lead to degeneration, the bones coming into contact with each other – the painful prelude to arthritic degenerative conditions.

Fibrous-articular cartilage is tough, inelastic and resistant to stretching, and is found in disc form, for example the intervertebral discs. These articular discs increase the stability and complexity of movement at a joint; without them, two bones would not fit each other congruently. Discs may also act as shock absorbers within joints or help the spreading of synovial fluid between the load-bearing surfaces of joints under considerable pressure, for example, the knee joint in running and the shoulder in the handstand.

A cartilaginous plate, called an epiphyseal plate, separates the end of a growing bone (epiphysis) from the shaft (diaphysis). This is of central importance to the discussion of correct and safe movement and will be looked at in some detail in the next chapter.

TENDONS

Tendons join muscle to bone, cartilage, ligaments or other connective tissue. They enable a muscle to act at a distance: for example, the muscles of the forearm can act on the fingers due to the tendinous attachments which pass through the wrist region.

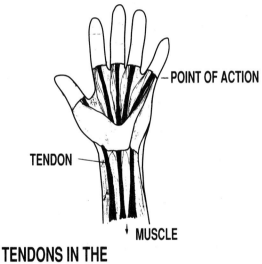

POINT OF ACTION

TENDON

↓ **MUSCLE**

TENDONS IN THE
WRIST – MUSCLE ACTION AT DISTANCE

Flattened or ribbon-shaped tendons are called aponeuroses. Many tendons, however, are cordlike. You can feel the biceps tendon just below the inside of the elbow where it attaches to the forearm; it feels very hard and you can easily get your finger and thumb round it if you put your arm at a right angle at the elbow.

The blood supply to tendons is rather poor but can be optimized by keeping them really warm and doing plenty of good movements. Micro-trauma over many years probably contributes to tendon rupture in later life. That is to say, many little tears weaken the tendon progressively until one day a comparatively minor incident might cause it to snap. This can be most spectacular an occasion for the onlookers, although being the victim is not pleasant. When playing basketball in my mid-thirties, my patella tendon snapped as I ran along the court. The sensation was an interesting one. At first I was sure someone had stuck out a foot and tripped me, but there was no player within ten feet. Then there was the noise, a really sharp crack, although not apparently as good as an Achilles tendon which often goes off like a gun. It all seemed so minor an incident until I tried to get to my feet and the pain hit me. Incredulously, I watched my patella move up my thigh as the quadriceps went into spasm. Good stretching, warm ups and warm downs are important protective procedures for tendons and I wish I had done a lot more as a younger sportsman!

MUSCLE

Muscle is not just a mass of contracting tissue. All the supporting (not contracting) tissue is also part of the muscle. Indeed, it is this extra tissue which supports the muscle and transmits the tension of muscle contraction through tendons to the bone.

So muscles consist of bundles of muscle fibres enclosed in a sheath of deep fascia, which are attached to the bone either directly or by a tendon or by fibrous tissue such as fascia or the fibrous tissue of other muscles.

The contractile parts of a muscle fibre (ultrastructure is discussed below) are the myofibrils. Muscles responsible for a particular movement are known as *agonists*. Muscles acting in the opposed direction are *antagonists*.

The picture is, however, more complex than this because not all the muscles surrounding a joint will function as either agonists or antagonists. Some may not work at all in a particular movement, others may support the joint maintaining its stability, while others are actually causing the movement. In this situation they are acting more like ligaments do, restricting movement, but unlike ligaments, these muscles are of variable length and can produce variable tension.

The shoulder joint is an example of a joint where a considerable variety of movement is possible and in a number of directions. The fibrous capsule of the shoulder tends to be thinner and more lax than those of most other joints and thus the muscles become crucial to its stability. These shoulder-supporting muscles, for optimum performance, must stretch the required amount and then contract to support the joint in a given position. Muscles that are not moved through their full range on a regular basis tend to reduce in range. Adhesions between the connective tissue gradually build up and restrict the functional range. This may lead to a need to modify actions to extend the range artificially; for example, by using the back to enhance a restricted shoulder.

If your shoulder does not allow you to reach far enough backwards for an overhead or high tennis shot you may have to rely too heavily on back hyperextension, producing a potentially more dangerous position. The long-term prognostication

might then be chronic low back pain. All because the shoulder range was restricted and the skill modification was inappropriate.

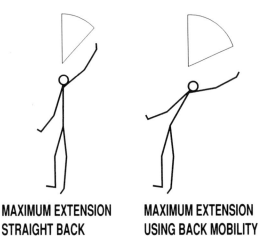

MAXIMUM EXTENSION   MAXIMUM EXTENSION
STRAIGHT BACK   USING BACK MOBILITY

REACH BACKWARDS

So, habitual activities may favour some movements and not others and over the years some functions may become less stable or even impossible. Stretching programmes can be used to re-educate and extend the functional capacity of joints by conditioning this tissue.

MULTI-JOINT MUSCLES

Some muscles pass over one joint and affect the movement of other joints. For example, the calf muscle, the gastrocnemius, which helps to flex the knee and plantarflex the ankle. Certain simultaneous movements at the joints over which they pass cannot occur because the muscles cannot shorten enough. The hamstrings cannot extend the hip and flex the knee at the same time. However, when the hip is flexed with the knee extended, the end of the hamstring is tautly drawn over the hip joint, causing it to take on the protective function of a ligament. At the other end of the muscle an automatic shortening contraction takes place that moves the knee joint.

These examples serve to illustrate the complexity of movements and the consequent need to establish a full range of movement in muscles so that they are not restricted in their application. Understanding that 'application' does not simply mean basic agonist activity but includes antagonists stretch, isometric support, secondary isotonic activities and the variable ligament function described above.

ULTRASTRUCTURE

The macro- or large anatomy of muscle and the other tissues associated with the joints, allows understanding of some of the limiting factors in an individual's movement range both actively and passively. It also starts to define the rationale for flexibility training and the appropriate techniques to use in that training. However, for a complete picture one needs to look at the arrangement of the sub-units which make up these tissues and appreciate how they function at the molecular level.

MUSCLE ULTRASTRUCTURE

The fundamental unit of contraction in skeletal muscle is the sarcomere which is diagrammatically represented below. Each sarcomere has within it a well-defined arrangement of protein molecules. The two main proteins are actin and myosin, which if viewed under the light microscope can be seen to be stacked in an overlapping way. Myosin being thicker

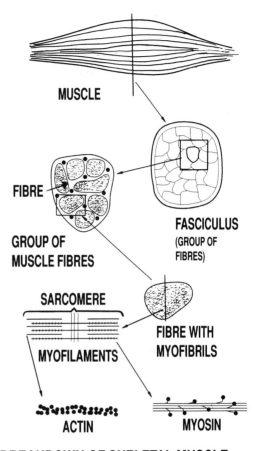

BREAKDOWN OF SKELETAL MUSCLE

than actin gives the stripped appearance typical in the myofilaments and myofibrils. As the stacking is not only precise within the sarcomere (myofilaments – myosin and actin) but also between adjacent sarcomeres and adjacent myofibrils (chains of sarcomeres) within the muscle cell (muscle fibre), so the stripped nature of this muscle is established.

In contraction, the actin and myosin molecules become activated and the resting length of the sarcomere is reduced as the actin slides further under the myosin. There is an all or nothing rule applying to contraction at the level of a muscle cell, so if the fibre is going to contract all sarcomeres contract in that cell.

In fact, defined groups of muscle cells innervated by a nerve will contract together or not contract at all. The range of strengths of contraction available to a muscle like the biceps, for example, will depend on the number of contracting groups called in by the nerves, the frequency with which they are told to contract, their biochemical state of readiness (nutrients etc.) and the total mass of sarcomeres. So the subtle range of actions available is not a function of degrees of contraction within sarcomeres, but the number and frequency of total contracting sarcomeres.

The relative position of the actin and myosin at the start of contraction is important in terms of the strength of contraction achievable. If the overlap between the molecules is small (stretched) then the number of active sites for energy conversion are also limited. Equally if the overlap goes too far (squashed) again there are limited active sites available between the molecules and less tension can be generated.

For a practical example of this try to support a weight using your biceps in three different positions. First support a heavy book in your hand just off the table with the elbow at right angles, then with the arm flat to the table (elbow about 5 degrees) and finally with your shoulder over your hand (elbow 135 degrees). You will feel the difference in how much harder it is at 5 and 135 degrees than at 90 degrees. Graphically this is shown below.

When we practise skills in sport we try to maintain a position which allows the most efficient use of the contractile processes. But often we are placed in a position

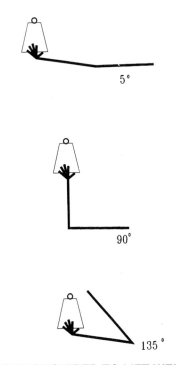

5°

90°

135°

EFFORT REQUIRED TO LIFT WEIGHT WITH JOINT AT DIFFERENT ANGLES

where the tissue is stretched out or squashed up. If training has not exploited these inefficient positions then we may not be able to withstand the outside forces. This at best may mean we lose the point at tennis or at worst sustain damage. Thus, strength training must be applied to the full range of muscle movements and as flexibility is increased so must strength at the new range.

Returning to the sarcomere, it seems it can be passively placed, stretched to about 120 per cent of its normal resting length and contracted to as much as 50 per cent of this resting value. So from the point of view of the contractile elements there is the potential for massive ranges of movement.

The longer the myofibril, the more

sarcomeres there are in a series and therefore the longer the muscle and the less restriction there will be to stretching. The increase in the girth of muscles will come from strength training but this implies more myofibrils and therefore more sarcomeres in parallel. This could also mean a smaller range of movement unless the strength has been achieved through full ranges of motion. If the sport has restricted ranges for some muscles it would be important to use training programmes to extend those ranges. For example, cycling has powerful but restricted leg movement ranges. The knee never fully extends in normal cycling which can cause imbalance between the medial and other aspects of the quadriceps. To avoid associated patella problems, cyclists should exercise the full range independently.

If one muscle becomes weak through neglect or injury, or if one muscle is allowed to hypertrophy and the other in a pair stays normally strong, this can create structural imbalance as the pull through the joints will not be even.

Clearly it is in the interest of every sports performer to encourage long muscles, that is a long series of sarcomeres. Habitual static positions such as sitting or immobilization through injury tend to restrict the growth of long myofibrils in those muscles held in a short position. Contrasting activities especially during growth periods will lessen the effect of some restrictive activities. Also where immobilization is necessary, then taking up the most stretched-out position will also encourage longer muscles to form. Certainly, as an early part of muscle rehabilitation after the acute effects are over, patients are encouraged to stretch the muscles and work full ranges within the bounds of pain.

It is recommended that the student of sports looks in more depth at muscular ultrastructure, as it will give a better insight into many aspects of sports performance.

CONNECTIVE TISSUE ULTRASTRUCTURE

As we have seen the muscle is bound in a mass of connective tissue, this tissue supports muscle fibres, forms a structure in which the blood and nerve tissue can run, and transmits the tension produced in contraction. It also acts as a defence mechanism and a storage depot but these functions are not of interest here.

Within a muscle one thinks of the contractile protein as being predominant but in fact there is a series of protein-based connective tissues which make up about 30 per cent of the total mass: the sarcolemma around the sarcomere; the endomysium around the individual fibres; the perimysium around the small bundles of fibres; and, the epimysium encasing the whole muscle.

Where the muscles taper towards their tendons these tissues become greater in proportion as the contractile elements reduce.

Two types of connective tissue are identified: fibrous and elastic. They are found in varying proportions in the fascia around the muscles, in tendons and ligaments, etc. The ways in which the elements of connective tissue are packed together, the number of cross links between fibres, the properties of the two major fibres and the associated ground substances, all act together in determining how they react to applied forces.

The two fibres to be considered are collagen and elastin.

Collagen is a protein arranged into fibres in a similar way to muscle however, it is non-contractile. The molecule has a triple helix form and the molecules are arranged in parallel bands within the fibril. The collagen fibre construction has the major properties of high tensile strength and very little extensibility. Thus, although capable of withstanding large forces, it only lengthens a little and then will break.

Both within the molecule and between the fibres it makes up, collagen forms cross links. This adds greatly to its tensile strength and restricts the stretch in it. As you get older collagen tends to get thicker, have more cross links and also changes in its molecular form. This all adds to the 'stiffness' of ageing.

The other influence on collagen seems to be the ground substances associated with it: a gel-like non-fibrous material which contains water and acts as a lubricant to the fibres. It tends to act, therefore, in the opposite way to the cross links, allowing more movement.

Immobilization seems to increase the cross linking, probably due to changes in ground substances, and thus tends to increase resistance to movement. On the other hand stretching tends to keep better distances between the fibres and maintain a fuller range of motion by reducing cross-link formation.

Elastin connective tissue has elastic fibres as the principle component and forms a major part of the sarcolemma. The structure of the molecules in elastic tissue is less well understood than collagen. They do form a rope-like structure but are not organized as in collagen. They do have cross links but with coiled chains allowing stretch. They seem important in returning tissue to its original shape and maintaining it after forces have been removed. Energy can be stored in this tissue and then used in the recoil, for example, in plyometrics.

With ageing, the structure tends to become more fragmented and there is a general mineralization, both of which reduce the elasticity of the tissue.

Johns and Wright (1962) indicate that the resistance to movement in a joint can be attributed to the skin (2 per cent), the tendon (10 per cent), the joint capsule (47 per cent) and the muscle and fascia (41 per cent). The relative amounts and packing structure of collagen and elastin fibres in these tissues form the basis for this resistance. Stretching will allow these tissues within the muscle/fascia complex to be maintained in the optimum condition, thus reducing the muscle and fascia component of the total resistance to movement.

SEXUAL DIMORPHISM IN FLEXIBILITY

A chapter on anatomy would not be complete without addressing the question of whether females are more flexible than males. There are two aspects to this question. First, are females usually more flexible than males and second, is that because they are female?

Certainly from observation, females generally show more flexibility. Also, it is known that bone differences together with appropriate hormonal balance, assist in the carriage and birth of children by alterations to the range of motion.

A further observational point might be that, in general, the female skeletal structure is slight and the muscle bulk is less. These may act together in affording a less resistive morphology.

Having said all that, these points are marginal and the basic difference can be put down to habitual activities and societal pressures and norms. Certainly I have seen very flexible men who have achieved these abilities through training. If there is a sex difference it is not one which should or needs to restrict the activities appropriate to either sex.

The study of anatomy gives the student of sport the first part of the rationale on which to base training and performance strategies in general. For flexibility, specifically, it allows those who wish to be informed (and many are reluctant), a straightforward and essentially simple set of primary rules. These rules will be developed through looking next at the physiological (functional) and then the developmental (growth) constraints in Chapters 3 and 4 respectively.

REFERENCES

Alter, M. J., *Science of Stretching*, Human Kinetics, 1988

McNaught-Davis, J. P., *Developing Flexibility* (Resource Pack), National Coaching Foundation, 1986

Warwick, R. and Williams, P. L., *Gray's Anatomy*, 35th edn, Longman, 1973

Woods, B., *Structure of the Body* (Resource Pack), National Coaching Foundation, 1990

3

YOUR PHYSIOLOGICAL LIMITS

Physiology is the science of body functions in general, here we are concerned with the functioning of tissues and systems that impinge directly on safe flexibility improvement, so the nervous and muscular systems are of particular interest.

The physiological story, just like the anatomical one in Chapter 2, needs to identify for the coach and performer the constraints that set the limits for safe and effective flexibility training. The anatomy story tells us which tissues can be safely and usefully stretched and which tissues we need to avoid stretching. But before being in a position to plan and execute a good flexibility programme we need to know how to stretch. This 'how' should be based on sound physiological principles which fall into two areas. The first concerns the physical properties of the tissues under stretch: the *biophysical factors*. The second, the way the nervous system works in relation to human voluntary muscle, i.e what the central nervous system

(CNS) is telling the muscles to do: the *neurophysiological factors*.

BIOPHYSICAL FACTORS

The physical properties of muscle which are important in stretching and flexibility are those that relate to the specific goal of an increase in length. Frequently the term 'stretch' or 'stretching' is used in the text to convey a linear deformation of the tissue that increases that tissue's length.

To look further into the responses of tissue to stretching we need to refer to the laboratory evidence. Studies indicate that most, if not all, of the resistance to a stretch is derived from the extensive connective tissue framework and sheathing within and around the muscle and not from the contractile muscle fibre elements (Sapega et al. 1981). Connective tissue is composed of collagen fibres and ground substance matrix. There are two material physical properties of connective tissue that affect the type of stretch it can undergo – viscosity and elasticity. Viscosity is a property of 'flowability'. We might describe oil as being much more viscous than, say, water, because it flows less easily or more slowly down a surface. Elasticity, as in common use, refers to the combined factors of 'stretchiness and returnability'. Connective tissue is a visco-elastic material: when stretched it behaves as if it has both viscous and elastic elements connected in series.

VISCOUS ELEMENTS ▪ ➤ ELASTIC ELEMENTS ▪ ➤ TENSILE FORCE

The elastic elements enable recoverable (elastic) deformation while the viscous elements enable permanent (plastic) deformation. Sapega et al. (1981) represented

the elastic properties with a spring model and the viscous properties with a hydraulic cylinder model. A rubber band representing elastic and a lump of plasticine for viscous, are simple teaching aids.

ELASTIC PROPERTIES

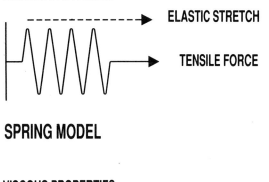

SPRING MODEL

VISCOUS PROPERTIES

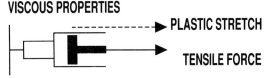

HYDRAULIC CYLINDER MODEL

There are various factors that influence the proportion of plastic and elastic stretch in connective tissue, the amount of applied force, the duration of applied force and the tissue temperature being the most important. For any stretching technique to be effective it must attack specifically the plastic/viscous properties of tissues because permanant changes in length are only achieved by a 'plastic deformation'. Conversely, a quick stretch only attacks the elastic elements which return (or tear) dependent on the force applied. Thus any sort of dynamic bouncing stretch is at best useless and at worst damaging.

When human tissue is put under stretch in the laboratory, minimal structural weakening occurs under lower forces and higher temperatures; maximal structural weakening occurs with higher forces and lower temperatures i.e., if the tissue is warm and has a low force applied you are less likely to experience damage than if the tissue is cold with a high force applied. Also if you apply low forces for a long period you get viscous (permanent) changes.

FACTOR	ELASTIC STRETCH	VISCOUS STRETCH
AMOUNT OF APPLIED FORCE	HIGH	LOW
DURATION OF APPLIED FORCE	SHORT	LONG
TISSUE TEMPERATURE	NORMAL	HIGHER

FACTORS INFLUENCING VISCO-ELASTIC BEHAVIOUR OF CONNECTIVE TISSUE

From a practical point of view the biophysical data tell us to stretch slowly and gently for an extended period when the tissue is warm. The tissue will act rather like the combination of an elastic band and a piece of plasticine but it is the plastic deformation that is required.

The practicalities of warming up are dealt with in other parts of the text, but the theory is worth a brief mention here. This warm-up thing is a 'perverse yet interesting physiological concern'. It is rather as if we have a good theoretical argument for it but little solid practical evidence confirming that it is, actually, beneficial in terms of sports performance. Nevertheless, warm-up should be a part of all training and performance. In flexibility work, certainly, attention to good warm-up as a matter of course is highly recommended. Warm-up has many theoretical advantages, as summarized in the very comprehensive *Sport Science Handbook* by Simon Jenkins.

Warm-up techniques are used to increase local muscle and total body (core) temperature before vigorous exercise ... It seems that an increase above normal core temperature of two degrees celsius is sufficient to produce the following physiological effects:
1. more rapid and complete dissociation of oxygen from haemoglobin and myoglobin;
2. acceleration of metabolic rate, leading to more efficient use of energy substrates;
3. reduction of muscle viscosity, leading to an improvement in the mechanical efficiency of muscular contractions;
4. greater speed and force of muscular contraction;
5. at the start of vigorous exercise, blood flow is directed more quickly to working skeletal muscle and away from the viscera; this is due to vasodilation [vasoconstriction in the viscera];
6. improvement in the delivery of energy substrates and removal of metabolic by-products, due to vasodilation;
7. nerve receptors are more sensitive and nerve impulses are transmitted at higher speed;
8. reduced risk of injury to muscle because of higher blood saturation;
9. improved flexibility, ability to improve flexibility, and reduce risk of injury due to increased extensibility of tendons, ligaments and other connective tissue.

NEUROPHYSIOLOGICAL FACTORS

In muscles, tendons and other structures of the joints, sense organs called proprioceptors are involved in precision movement and in the co-ordination of movement. It is necessary in the context of flexibility to understand the functioning of two types of these sense organs, namely muscle spindles and Golgi tendon organs. A sense organ receives information in one form and transmits it in an electrical form to other parts of the CNS where it can be dealt with. They are therefore forms of transducers, in this case picking up changes in length and/or the rate of change in length and/or tension within the muscle tendon complex, and sending off electrical impulses accordingly.

MUSCLE SPINDLES

Muscle spindles lie parallel to muscle fibres. They can either lie inside them, giving rise to intrafusal muscle fibres, or outside, forming extrafusal muscle fibres. The intrafusal spindles are sensitive to changes in muscle length and contain primary and secondary sensory endings. Sensory endings are the ends of nerves that send information in the form of nerve impulses to the cerebellum via the spinal cord. The primary sensory endings detect the velocity of the muscle fibre (the rate of stretch). The secondary sensory endings detect displacement of the muscle fibre (how much it has stretched).

When a muscle is stretched, the spindles are also stretched. The sensory endings within the spindles are deformed and this results in a volley of sensory impulses being sent to the cerebellum. (The message: *muscle being stretched rapidly, the joint may be damaged if not slowed up.*) Motor impulses are sent down the spinal cord to the muscle, causing a reflex contraction which resists the stretch. (The response: *muscle being stretched resist at all costs, contract quickly against the stretch.*) This is known as the stretch reflex (myotatic reflex) and is illustrated below.

An example of the stretch reflex is the

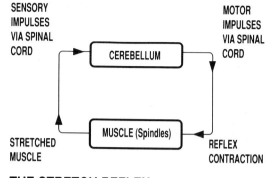

SENSORY IMPULSES VIA SPINAL CORD

MOTOR IMPULSES VIA SPINAL CORD

CEREBELLUM

MUSCLE (Spindles)

STRETCHED MUSCLE

REFLEX CONTRACTION

THE STRETCH REFLEX

'knee jerk reflex'. When the patellar tendon (which joins the quadriceps to the tibia bone of the lower leg) is tapped abruptly, the quadriceps are rapidly stretched. In accordance with the above diagram, a reflex contraction of the quadriceps occurs, producing the famous 'knee jerk'. Inventing a conscious relaxation can reduce the magnitude of the reflex jerk. This is all due to certain stimulation of the spindles via the gamma fibres. In other words, if you are very relaxed the higher centres in the brain reduce the sensitivity of the spindles. This appears to reset the spindles and reduces the responses. This could be thought of as a little like the effect of improved *détente* between West and East as we come out of the cold war: the spindles are the early warning systems against attack from the enemy, i.e. the tap on the tendon. The spinal response of aggressive resistance is modified (we hope), like that of Moscow or Washington, by the state of *détente* (relaxation).

The stretch reflex is a response to a stretch which has been applied passively. That is to say, the muscle is being stretched by an action which does not include an active contraction of an opposing muscle.

GOLGI TENDON ORGANS

Golgi tendon organs are found at the end of muscle fibres in the tendons. They are sensitive to changes in muscle tension as well as to changes in the length of the muscle. When a muscle contracts it stretches the tendon bundles and compresses the sensory nerve endings attached to the tendon organs, sending nerve impulses to the cerebellum. The tendon organs produce an inhibitory response to the stretch reflex. If the muscle stretch lasts at least six seconds, the Golgi tendon organs respond to the change in length and tension by sending their sensory impulses to the cerebellum. The motor impulses from the cerebellum cause a reflex relaxation in the muscle.

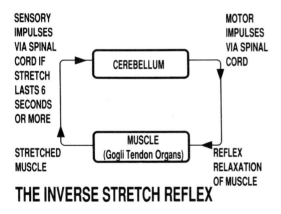

THE INVERSE STRETCH REFLEX

The impulses from the Golgi tendon organs are able to override those coming from the muscle spindles. Therefore the muscle can relax after the initial reflex contraction or resistance to the change in length. This Golgi tendon organ response, the inverse stretch reflex, is referred to as autogenic inhibition. It is a phenomenon that underlies the rationale for stretching both static and proprioceptive neuromuscular facilitation (PNF), although in

PNF there are other aspects as well (*see below*).

Everything discussed so far in this section refers to the passive situation where muscles have not been working and it thus applies to the normal flexibility training method of slow stretching. However, if we look for a minute at the active situation when voluntary muscle movements are being used it can tell us about the rationale for an 'advanced' form of stretching known as proprioceptive neuromuscular facilitation (PNF).

In order to do this, there are two other neurophysiological phenomena which should be considered: Autogenic Reflex (AI) and Reciprocal Inhibition (RI).

AI is a phenomenon associated with contracting a muscle which is being stretched or about to be stretched further and leads to a relaxation of that muscle (see Chapter 8). Similar neurophysiological processes underlie both AI and the Inverse Stretch Reflex (discussed above). These processes involve the Golgi tendon organs.

The best way to understand RI is to consider the stretch reflex in an active situation. When you kick a ball or do any active muscle work, the stretch reflex must be inhibited. If it was not, then every time you started a movement the opposing muscle(s) would be stretched and immediately contract and act against the action. The inverse stretch reflex would not be any good here as a six-second delay would be quite useless for normal active situations.

There must be another mechanism of the nervous system at work in active muscle actions. This mechanism is known as reciprocal inhibition (RI) and all it means is that the agonist (active muscle) sends sensory impulses as it is contracting via the CNS to the antagonist muscle(s) which inhibit that muscle from contracting.

An example may make it clear: you are about to kick a ball so the hamstrings draw your lower leg back and up. As they contract the quadriceps are stretched. Now, if the quadriceps started contracting against the hamstrings, one or other of the muscles would tear. RI allows the quadriceps to stay relaxed and only start contracting as the hamstrings are finishing their movement. At this point the RI is reversed and the hamstrings allow themselves to be stretched as the foot swings towards the ball.

Interestingly enough you can get a sharp reminder that the stretch reflex is inhibited if someone takes the ball away and you miss the kick! Under these circumstances the normal sensory input of contact with the ball, which would be the signal to switch off the quadriceps and initiate the hamstrings to slow the leg down by contracting, are missing. Also the active nature of the movement has inhibited the stretch reflex apparent in passive stretching, so the leg swings on until the soft tissue eventually takes the strain . . . and it hurts. You have learnt the skill so well that it is unlikely that the visual input of the ball not being there will be picked up and used to save your knee. When good at a skill we rarely 'watch the ball' that well; instead, we use our eyes for tactical information and automatically carry out the basic skills. Another example, non-sporting in this case, is the missed step on the stairs, usually in the dark, on steps you know well but miscount.

What does this tell us about stretching techniques? The theory is that by actively working a muscle you can initiate a relaxation in the opposing muscle which can then be used to achieve an easier and larger stretch in that opposing muscle. Two PNF methods are mentioned in this text as they represent the normal sporting uses of this technique. They will be discussed in full in Part Two, but the theory on which they are based is simply the neurophysiology described here.

A muscle has to be able to contract from the full range of possible starting lengths through the course of any particular game or sport – especially where the skills involved are open ones like tennis. But even in closed-skill sports like golf you cannot always rely on an even and unrestricted stance. Just imagine a game of tennis where you find yourself out of position and have to play a forehand very close to the body or at full stretch. In these situations can you hit or strike as hard? No, you know you can't from experience. That is, of course, why the coaching manuals tell you where you should be in relation to the ball; they give you the ideal mechanical position. But life is not like that . . . nor is sport.

At this point it is necessary to refer to some micro-anatomy or ultrastructure and molecular biochemistry. These fundamental physiological facts of exercise have been briefly described in Chapter 2, and can be seen in much more detail in most good exercise physiology texts.

The contractile elements of muscle are arranged with considerable and beautiful precision. The major molecular players in this microscopic performance are aligned so that the energy source and the two halves of the machine that uses the energy are in close proximity. Like the two halves of a rugby scrum or the opposing lines of American Football players they are energized by a simple trigger, which in this analogy is the movement of the ball. The two halves of a scrum if not aligned correctly will not function – there is just nowhere for the ball to go. But put together properly the potential energy can be released by the merest flick of the scrumhalf's wrists.

Similarly, the precise molecular arrangement of muscle is important in the efficient release of energy – when in the mid-relaxed position you have many aligned energy converters, like chains of quiescent front rows waiting for the ball of energy to start them pushing. As you move towards the extremes of fibre length (stretched out or pushed together), so the numbers of aligned energy converts (crossbridges) reduces.

When a muscle contracts the maximum strength it can generate will be determined (everything else being equal) by the length of the fibres at the time of contraction. In the graph below, this relationship between starting length of muscle and maximum strength able to be generated is shown. This actually changes from muscle to muscle dependent on its anatomical form. Nevertheless, as a concept this idealized tension/length curve makes the point. If the fibres are at their shortest the active molecular elements overlap too much and the maximum number of pulling connections cannot be made. Equally, if the fibres start to work when fully stretched (longest), they have few opportunities to make interconnections and the tension created is low. Somewhere between these extremes is the optimum starting length for maximum tension output.

This idea becomes important when we consider strength and flexibility in Chapter 5.

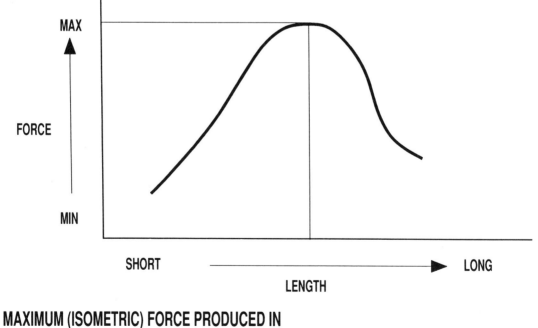

MAXIMUM (ISOMETRIC) FORCE PRODUCED IN MUSCLE AT DIFFERENT STARTING LENGTHS (GENERAL SHAPE)

SUMMARY

The connective tissue supporting muscle from the main resistance to stretch; this resistance is increased by a stretch reflex.

Relaxation can reduce the magnitude of the stretch reflex, which can be more fully overcome by the inverse stretch reflex which takes about six seconds to elicit.

Slow, gentle, continuous force applied to warm tissue will produce the permanent changes needed for increased flexibility.

These stretching strategies are consistent with the safe improvement of flexibility in immature, mature and ageing muscle tissue. Thus anatomy and physiology points toward Slow and Static Stretching (SASS) as the ideal method to improve flexibility safely and effectively.

REFERENCES

Alter, M. J., *Science of Stretching*, Human Kinetics, 1988

Astrand, P-O. and Rodahl, K., *Textbook of Work Physiology: Physiological Bases of Exercise,* 3rd edn, McGraw-Hill, 1988

de Vries, M. A., *Physiology of Exercise,* 4th edn, Brown & Co., 1986

McArdle, W., Katch, F. and Katch, V., *Exercise Physiology: Energy, Nutrition, and Human Performance*, Lea and Febiger (Philadelphia), 1986

McNaught-Davis, J. P., *Developing Flexibility* (Resource Pack), National Coaching Foundation, 1986

NCF Coaching Handbook 3, *Physiology and Performance*, National Coaching Foundation, 1988

Sapega, A., Quendenfield, T. C., Moyer, R. A. and Butler, R. A., 'Biophysical Factors in Range-of-Motion Exercise', *Physician and Sportsmedicine* 9(12): pp. 57–65, 1981

4

HEALTH AND FLEXIBILITY

The tissues discussed in the chapters on anatomy and physiology, are fully developed, mature and adult, rather than immature tissue. It takes more than twenty years to develop the full adult skeleton and until this development is complete it is immature tissue that will be exposed to the stresses of sport. The real significance of the immaturity of tissue is not so much in the tissue functions *per se*, because these may be basically 'adult' from the start, but more in their arrangement and interconnections. During development the many systems have different capacities from their adult versions. Some of the capacities, like tissue regeneration, may put the young sports performer at an advantage, however, others may only seem to be an advantage, or be open to abuse or even be a positive disadvantage.

Later in life the adult tissue starts to deteriorate progressively and again the capacities change and the potential for abuse may become significant once more.

The understanding of this developmental

process in relation to the capacity of children and older people to partake safely in activity, should be of concern to all those who encourage exercise. It is simplistic to class all exercise together as either good or bad or, indeed, healthy or appropriate for everyone. The media and advertisers may like the simple concept, but 'real people' would do well to develop a more educated understanding.

There are differences in the anatomical and physiological condition of both the young and the old and these have a general bearing on the approach to, and practice of, sport, as well as a specific significance to flexibility work.

THE YOUNG BODY UP TO TWENTY BUT ESPECIALLY PRE-PUBERTY

The following brief description of skeletal development and maturation highlights both the importance of careful coaching of the young sportsman and also shows how chronic pathological conditions associated with ageing may be avoided.

PRIMARY SITES OF OSSIFICATION

The normal pattern of bone development starts in the unborn child from around the eighth foetal week when spots of X-ray opaque material can be seen at the centres of what will become the long bones; these are primary sites of ossification. The rest of the future bone is transparent to X-ray because it is cartilaginous. These 'cartilage models' grow through foetal life, childhood and puberty, with the calcified bony parts lengthening until eventually they grow to the ends of the shafts. During this process, which takes between twelve and twenty-one years to complete, the cartilage parts are pliable and much softer than the bony parts; they are therefore very vulnerable to damage.

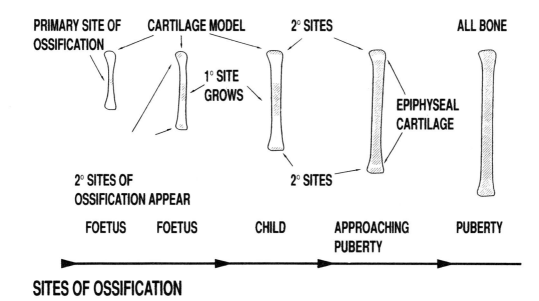

SITES OF OSSIFICATION

SECONDARY SITES OF OSSIFICATION

At some stage, dependent upon the bone, the individual and environmental factors, a second point at which calcification of the cartilage takes place is usually established at the two ends, or caps, of the bone. This is known as a secondary site of ossification, and it will eventually fuse with the growing bone from the primary site.

Some secondary sites may appear while the baby is still in the womb, many do not appear until early childhood. Fusion of the caps and shafts marks the point of maturity

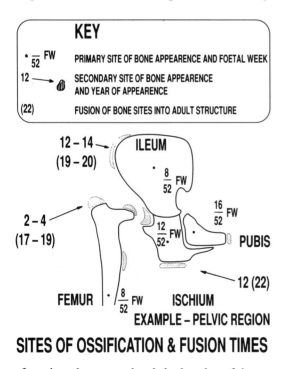

KEY

• $\frac{FW}{52}$	PRIMARY SITE OF BONE APPEARENCE AND FOETAL WEEK	
12 → ⬧	SECONDARY SITE OF BONE APPEARENCE AND YEAR OF APPEARENCE	
(22)	FUSION OF BONE SITES INTO ADULT STRUCTURE	

12 – 14
(19 – 20)　　　**ILEUM**

$\frac{8}{52}$ FW

$\frac{16}{52}$ FW

2 – 4
(17 – 19)

$\frac{12}{52}$ FW

PUBIS

12 (22)

FEMUR　• $\frac{8}{52}$ FW　　**ISCHIUM**

EXAMPLE – PELVIC REGION

SITES OF OSSIFICATION & FUSION TIMES

for that bone and adult levels of bone strength. For most bones this point is reached at puberty, between eleven and sixteen years, with boys tending to mature later than girls.

Thus muscles which we think of as

being firmly attached via tendon to bones are, in reality, often attached to cartilage. These muscles if pulled too hard either passively or by active contraction can disrupt these growth areas. Over-strong muscles can literally pull the epiphyseal (growth) plates away or disrupt them so that unsightly and often restrictive extra bone growth takes place.

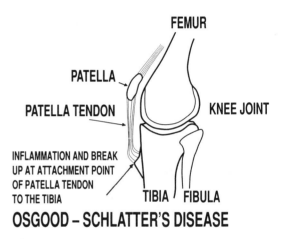

FEMUR

PATELLA

PATELLA TENDON

KNEE JOINT

INFLAMMATION AND BREAK
UP AT ATTACHMENT POINT
OF PATELLA TENDON
TO THE TIBIA

TIBIA　**FIBULA**

OSGOOD – SCHLATTER'S DISEASE

This often seems to be associated with young people, like footballers, playing and training day after day, basically doing too much exercise and making the muscle too strong for the junction. In other cases, like spondylolisthesis, the crumbling of spinal bones may be due to continually stretching using wrong methods. Good stretching would prevent such damage.

An added risk in sport is the effect of non-symmetrical activities where training and performance tend to favour one side or set of muscles over another. Throwing events, racket sports, etc., rely on a dominant side, and training for these may tend to encourage this one-sided development. This is true for all sports performers whatever their ages but is likely to be more significant in the immature and thus growing individual. There is a strong case for all-round development alongside the specific skills of a particular sport. Stretching has a part to play in minimizing the effects of any imbalance in muscle development and thus can be used to reduce the harmful effects of any over-emphasis inherent in some sports. A stronger muscle or a shorter muscle may have significantly more resting tone and progressively affect the alignment of the joints through which it acts. Such an imbalance in, say, the spine may in time predispose an individual towards a 'scoliosis' for example.

It should be remembered that in some body regions bones naturally take longer to mature than others – the pelvis, for example, is a site of fairly late bone maturity, fusion of some of these bony aspects occuring in the early twenties. Large powerful muscle groups are, therefore, pulling on immature skeletal areas all through the most intensive training periods of the young sports performer's life.

In this case the susceptibility to injury goes well beyond childhood.

All children and most young adults have, to some extent, an immature bone structure during the early years of their sporting lives. During this time, and particularly pre-puberty when, for example, gymnasts achieve most of their extra flexibility, the skeleton is easily damaged. The epiphyseal areas, bone–cartilage–bone junctions, are very vulnerable to the disruption that can be caused by over-strengthening muscles and ballistic stretching for flexibility.

This disruption may not necessarily be accompanied by serious pain or, where pain occurs, it may be erroneously associated with other things. Again we see the

importance of making correct decisions about how one trains.

How does all this square up with the need to encourage children to get into the habit of activity so that it stays with them into later life? Recent British research reports children generally do disturbingly little by way of exercise (Armstrong, 1989). Nevertheless those who are committed to exercise may do too much (McNaught-Davis, 1990). We are all searching for the happy medium, enough exercise but equally avoiding sowing the seeds of chronic long-term damage.

Some research does seem to indicate that specialization when too young is associated with more injury and does not actually produce better performance. In other words, in many activities you can get a good player from a later specialization. A general physical fitness based on many activities can be used as the basis for later specialization. What this means is that, in general terms, one should encourage the younger sports performers to ring the changes by doing various types of activity rather than just one. If you play hockey all the while you might expect to get round-shouldered because you look down at the ball for hours on end. If you played a bit of netball this 'kyphosis' might be avoided – but you will also be playing less hockey. Nevertheless both fitness and muscle development will be stimulated equally by both these sports (or others) but in a more rounded way than one sport would do.

At the extreme, the work expected of some children does seem very dubious in view of their long-term development. Our own research on gymnastics has produced some very interesting, if rather frightening, statistics.

INJURED GYMNASTS

VARIABLE (N=100)	MEAN	ST.D.	MINIMUM	MAXIMUM
AGE IN YEARS	13.14	2.20	8.00	17.75
YEARS GYMNASTICS	6.00	2.52	2.00	11.00
HOURS TRAINING/WEEK	16.79	4.13	8.08	25.75
DAYS TRAINING	4.52	0.66	3.00	7.00

(Adapted from Goodway et al. 1989)

Thus we see that many young people are hardly doing any worthwhile activity at all, while others like the gymnasts above seem to be specializing when very young and possibly training too hard.

To be optimum development needs the stimulation of exercise, yet can be easily disrupted by too much. Bone growth patterns, for example, tend to respond to habitual movement forces. If safety considerations are disregarded, extra flexibility may be achieved by pushing the cartilaginous areas of joints too far. Although this will achieve some apparent increase, there is a strong belief among sports medical personnel that the long-term implications of these practices can be serious. The motivation to do a sport is often wonderfully high amongst many young people and their parents are pleased to support such wholesome activity. This momentum should be exploited by the sports organizer for the good of both the short- and long-term health and fitness of the child – and not be abused for the glorification of winning at all costs.

It is not possible to give a prescription for every child because they are all different and so will be their responses to activity. However, the body gives signals and each athlete should be taught to listen to and feel these signals. Pain, for example, is not a sign that everything is all right, quite the opposite. Training should not be based on the idea that pain is a signal that you are working at the right intensity – it means quite the reverse.

With flexibility work – that is stretching – the limit of a stretch should be the point of resistance, before pain is felt. If the movements to reach that point are jerky or bouncy, then the 'point of pain' tends to become the signal, rather than the 'point of resistance'.

If you push yourself only once or twice a week you know the point of pain and try to avoid it. If every time you exercise (and that may be for some youngsters 2–4 hours a day) you go to the pain area – you get used to it – and in time the pain does not seem so bad. The question is, does that indicate no damage is being done or no damage is being felt?

THE DECLINING YEARS

The media, advertising and the 'health agencies' are all peddling their active-lifestyle and 'it's-never-too-late-to-start' approaches, trying to get the middle and older age groups into jogging and weight training. Their individual motives may not all be as laudible as the up-front one of getting everyone healthy – but that need not concern us here.

The problems for this group may be many and various, but the results of good exercise can be very real. One problem is the relationship of flexibility to the processes of 'anatomical and physiological ageing'.

As one gets older muscles and connective tissue tend to shorten, reducing the functional range of movement. Simple every-day activities such as tying one's shoe-laces can no longer be done with ease.

Certain tissue, like cartilage, shows greater calcification and, therefore, become less resistant or less able to absorb forces or be squeezed as much. This tends to restrict the useful range of motion and joints are less easy to move, particularly as the cartilage may be worn away as well.

The joints which seem particularly susceptible to these symptoms are the knees and lower back. Pathological conditions such as rheumatoid arthritis or non-pathological, degenerative conditions such as osteo-arthritis may develop. The spinal column loses its elasticity and compressing tolerance as one gets older and this can be hastened by inappropriate exercises.

Although these ageing factors are natural, their onset and speed of development can be delayed by maintaining sensible activity, avoiding obesity and in particular using stretching to optimize the range of movement and encourage circulation.

NATURAL EXTREMES OF FLEXIBILITY

EXCESSIVE

Some people are 'double jointed' or, much more correctly, hypermobile. This can seem a considerable advantage in some sports and coaches may well be pleased to get hold of a few hypermobile children. In actual fact, in many cases, the advantages are outweighed by the disadvantages.

Hypermobility may be a natural phenomenon and can be tested by some straight-forward tests, as shown below.

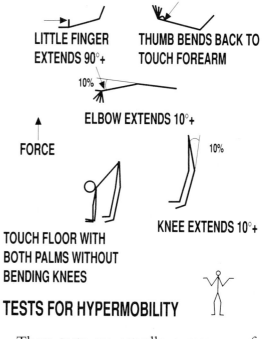

LITTLE FINGER EXTENDS 90°+

THUMB BENDS BACK TO TOUCH FOREARM

10%

ELBOW EXTENDS 10°+

FORCE

10%

KNEE EXTENDS 10°+

TOUCH FLOOR WITH BOTH PALMS WITHOUT BENDING KNEES

TESTS FOR HYPERMOBILITY

These tests are actually a measure of flexibility as they take place through the normal plane of movements. However, they evidently do correlate with joint laxity, and this laxity is the real danger to these individuals.

Hypermobility will tend to be in the majority of joints but in some cases may be confined to just one or two. As a natural phenomenon it is explained in terms of the laxity of connective tissue supporting joints (ligaments, capsules), and may also be due to abnormalities of the bony surfaces. This particular genetic characteristic must be thought of as a potentially pathogenic one, in that the extensive extra range of movement that is allowed predisposes the individual to partial or even complete dislocation. Two major points need to be made about this condition.

First, the flexibility of these individuals needs to be restricted, or at least protected against, by building up muscle to help support the lax joint tissue. Second, with regard to the prevention of injury, it is suggested that these individuals are likely to be at greater risk and should avoid contact sports or sports with a habitually excessive range of movements. Once a joint has passed outside its normal range it becomes very unstable.

Some hypermobility may not, in every case, be naturally occurring but rather the result of excessive, inappropriate flexibility training within the sport. In this case, the hypermobility probably would have been achieved prior to the calcification of the joints and thus is a problem amongst children, especially pre-puberty.

It is easy to see the following scenario happening:

Parents of a very flexible child (hyperflexible – but they do not know it) may see some gymnastics on television and love the idea of their offspring being involved in that sport. After all, as they find out, this can be an interest for their child ten or twenty hours a week, and it is under adult supervision, indoors and clean – what could be better?

The coaches will be pleased to take such a promising newcomer and see her natural flexibility as an asset. The lack of strength to control the movements may not be seen as a disadvantage or danger as she is new and will need time to develop strength.

So, becoming a squad member, she gains respect from the other members because she can do a much bigger range of movements than the rest. She may even be used as the example to make the others try harder. But they can't compete. However much they try our girl can always push it a bit further.

The squad works for the same amount of time on each part of their training so she does all the flexibility work they do.

Much later she finds in competition she can't get the scores the others do, so works harder still on everything. It may be about now or some years later when she has given up (because she went into puberty and got bumps where she used to be flat or got fed up because she did not make the regional squad) that the pains start. The damage to joints cannot always be felt at the time it's happening.

Not all coaches would have acted like this. They may well recognize the problem and at best advise another sport or at least take her out of flexibility and give her extra strength classes.

This is a ficticious story, but hypermobility does have some very real consequences in terms of injury. Certainly there is a good case here for using weight training to try to acquire joint protection not provided by the lax ligament.

There is at least one side issue from the story. That is that *any competition* in flexibility is really dangerous and counterproductive for all concerned. By definition flexibility training and testing should be relaxed and not related to scoring better than someone else.

LIMITED

Just as there is the extreme excessive level of flexibility there is the opposite extreme – hypomobility or stiff jointedness. This is an unusual tightness of soft tissue around the joints. It can be due, for example, to particular abnormalities of bone restricting the normal range of motion.

There is a positive association between the level of stiffness in a joint and the likelihood of getting a strained muscle or sprained ligament. This is hardly surprising, as any restricted range requires movement patterns to speed up and slow down faster, and requires the individual to work nearer the extreme edges of his movement potential. The mechanical stresses are therefore more intense and thus tissue breakdown is more likely to occur.

Clearly flexibility work will get the most out of the tissue but cannot be expected to gain ranges beyond that set by the specific tissue's potential for stretching.

If individuals find that their flexibility is not improving even with plenty of training, it may be due to pathological adhesions which will need to be broken down by medical treatments. There is a nice article by Prichard (1987) concerning this problem among swimmers which is recommended. It is interesting to note an observation from this article:

We also find that the stiffest athletes stretch the least, and all athletes stretch the joints that are loose and ignore the ones that are tight.

A very human trait to do the things that come easy and ignore the others.

A decrease in flexibility over the years might be expected due to the ageing process, but as we see below this is not inevitable if flexibility work is maintained.

FLEXIBILITY AND INJURY

PREVENTION

Although throughout the text passing reference has been made to the relationships between flexibility and injury, it seems appropriate to dedicate at least a short section to this topic.

Judging from the literature available it seems fairly uncontentious to state that flexibility training and stretching are seen as a major factor in the prevention and rehabilitation of sports injury.

Even those writers who deny it has a major role to play in their sport (which, of course, it does) will accept flexibility as important in injury prevention:

Believe it or not, this (flexibility) is not a prime factor in squash, but it is important to prevent injury (Taylor, *Squash,* Pelham Books, 1985).

In the context of this discussion it is irrelevant whether the injury is sport specific or just a domestic or work accident. What is important is that through flexibility the sports performer can avoid injury, or rehabilitate injury effectively and quickly.

Avoiding injury in sport and in other situations can often be seen to relate to the efficiency of muscular action and reaction. Flexibility training is recognized as a way of helping to secure muscular efficiency.

Where research has cast doubt on this assumed positive relationship between stretching for flexibility and the ability to avoid muscle injury, for example Levine et al. (1987), there has often been a question mark over the techniques of stretching employed. Perhaps we should be more pedantic about how we say these things and emphasize that **correct** flexibility training can reduce the incidents of injury.

Clearly by far the biggest weight of professional opinion, if not always conclusive empirical evidence, is in favour of flexibility training preventing injury.

An effective injury prevention program for any athlete contains attention to warm-up with appropriate strengthening and stretching exercises (Moynes, 1983).

It is important when thinking about these relationships between injury and flexibility to be clear about what is meant by the terms used. Flexibility is a function of the tightness or otherwise of the muscle, tendon and connective tissue. Flexibility training is (should be) directed exclusively at this muscle complex. Laxity on the other hand relates to the level of instability in a joint and is associated with the construction of the joint and its ligamentous tissue.

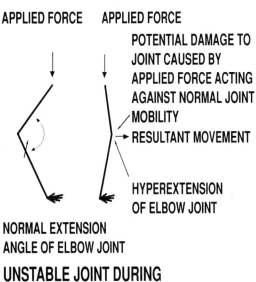

APPLIED FORCE   APPLIED FORCE

POTENTIAL DAMAGE TO JOINT CAUSED BY APPLIED FORCE ACTING AGAINST NORMAL JOINT MOBILITY

RESULTANT MOVEMENT

HYPEREXTENSION OF ELBOW JOINT

NORMAL EXTENSION ANGLE OF ELBOW JOINT

UNSTABLE JOINT DURING HYPEREXTENSION

As Steiner (1987) points out so clearly and simply, when we use hypomobility tests as a measure of joint laxity, we often do so with tests applied in the normal plane of movement, in other words, flexibility tests. To really look at laxity the test needs to be applied to the ligamentous not the muscle compartments and therefore across the planes of normal movement. The assumption is, of course, that the overlap between the two is enough to make the tests useful and to some extent, at least, that is true.

Injury to hypermobile joints would not be expected to be prevented through flexibility work as in these particular cases it is a restriction to movement that is required. The stability of the hypermobile joint at the extremes of normal motion will be particularly vulnerable, so this is why strength rather than flexibility would be appropriate training. Also it would be sensible to avoid sports where forces might be applied across these unstable joints, e.g. contact sports.

The prevention of injury for the sports performer comes down to eight factors and flexibility has a role in the first four:

1. Appropriate levels of fitness for the standard and type of sport being performed.
2. Skills appropriate to the standard and type of sport.
3. Balance between the strength and length of muscles acting on each joint.
4. Sufficient rest periods between bouts of exercise.
5. Using good quality equipment and checking it before use.
6. Eating a sensible diet, high in carbohydrates. Avoiding fad diets.
7. Playing sports appropriate to your age and body type.

8. Luck.

Only No. 8 above is directly beyond your control and includes the standard of refereeing and the other players. Although 'luck' may seem a rather funny factor to bother with it is important that people realize that risk of injury is part and parcel of sport – and most people probably like a small risk.

There is a popular golfing story where a professional, accused of being lucky, said that the more he practised the luckier he got. With injury, too, the more you attend to the first seven points above the less No. 8 will matter.

Flexibility training has specific importance in all of the first four factors as we have seen from the discussion in the previous chapters.

REHABILITATION

Flexibility training through stretching is an important modality used the world over by physiotherapists. This is not a medical text so this is not dealt with in any depth here, but a few general points are in order.

After an injury to muscle has occurred and repair is taking place, one wishes to maintain the original length of the tissue. By incorporating stretching in the rehabilitation the tissue will be encouraged to form in a long state and cross adhesions will be reduced, thus the eventual resistance to movement, associated with the injury, is reduced.

At the same time as wishing to rehabilitate the muscle, there is the question of the proprioceptors as well. The new relationships between length and tension have to be re-learnt and stretching can form an important aspect of this learning process by giving information for reference once the muscles are used fully again. Physiotherapists might use 'wobble-board' exercises to assist their training.

Relaxation may be difficult in the damaged tissue and again this will be encouraged by gentle stretching.

Thus it is important that sports people comply with stretching regimes which have been set up by their therapists to help achieve full and effective recovery. Through these processes the performer can expect to re-establish balance and function in the muscular system although that process may have to be an extended one. In some cases proprioceptive neuromuscular facilitation (PNF) techniques will be used, to enhance the speed with which this final full recovery can be achieved.

REFERENCES

Armstrong, N., Balding, J., Bray, S., Gentle, P. and Kirby, B., 'The Physical Activity Patterns of 10 and 13 Year Old Children', paper given at 14th International Seminar on Pediatric Work Physiology, Leuven, Belgium, 1989

Brobeck, J. R. (editor), *Best and Taylor's Physiological Basis of Medical Practice,* 10th edn, Williams and Wilkins, 1980

Goodway, J. D., McNaught-Davis, J. P. and White, J., 'The distribution of injuries among young female gymnasts in relation to selected training and environmental factors', in *Children and Exercise XIV*, edited by G. Beunen et al., Band 4 Schriftenreihe der Hamburg-Mannheimer-Stiftung fur Informationsmedizin, Enke Verlag, 1989

Jenkins, S. P. R., *Sports Science Handbook*, Sunningdale, 1990

Levine, M., Lombardo, J., McNeeley, J. and Anderson, T., 'An Analysis of Individual Stretching Programs of Inter-Collegiate Athletes', *Physician and Sportsmedicine* 15(3): pp. 132–6, 1987

McArdle, W., Katch, F. and Katch, V., *Exercise Physiology: Energy, Nutrition, and Human Performance,* Lea and Febiger (Philadelphia), 1986

McNaught-Davis, J. P., *Developing Flexibility* (Resource Pack), National Coaching Foundation, 1986

McNaught-Davis, J. P., *Developing Flexibility* (Video), Brighton Polytechnic, Media Services, Watts Bld., Brighton

McNaught-Davis, J. P., Goodway, J. D. and White, J., 'Training and Injury in Female Gymnastics', in the Proceedings of the International Congress on Youth, Leisure and Physical Activity and Kinanthropometry IV, 1990

Moynes, D. R., 'Prevention of Injury to the Shoulder Through Exercises and Therapy', *Clinics in Sports Medicine* 2(2): pp413–22, 1983

Nehrer, S., 'Comparative Investigation of Hip Joint Mobility in the Different Sports of Swimming, Cycling and Running', *Oesterreichisches Journal Fuer Sport-Medizin* 16(1): pp23–9, 1988

Prichard, B., 'Increasing Your Range', *Swimming Technique*, pp7–10, Feb–Ap. 1987

Prichard, B., Stretching for Speed, *Swimming Technique*, pp32–6, May–July 1987

Russell, K., 'Increasing Joint Range of Movement in Young Athletes', presented to the British Association of National Coaches, Birmingham, December 1985

Steiner, M. E., 'Hypermobility and Knee Injuries', *Physician and Sportsmedicine*, 15(6): pp159–65, 1987

Warwick, R. and Williams, P. L., *Gray's Anatomy*, 35th edn, Longman, 1973

FITNESS AND FLEXIBILITY

5

Stretching exercises are primarily for conditioning muscles in order to prepare them for other forms of training and (sport) performance. They may have, as we have seen, plenty of benefit in themselves because they can help to reduce injury from accidental overstretching, allow a larger useful range of motion and so on.

The major sporting benefits to be gained from 'dedicated and specific' flexibility training are to be seen in the results of combining the extra flexibility with other forms of training. In other words, by doing good flexibility work you do a number of important performance related things.

First, you reduce the resistance to movement within the muscles themselves, creating the potential for faster movement which will then be realized specifically through speed training.

Second, you increase the range over which a muscle has the potential to act, and this will be realized by further training, in this case, strength programmes.

Third, for the endurance athlete, there are the advantages related to preparing muscles for efficient repetition of action. This allows for maximum reduction of energy usage, balanced muscle action and enhanced recovery.

Finally there are the skill acquisition and production advantages. When you try to learn new skills or modify old skills, the muscles will respond better if they have been prepared and primed for action – flexibility training is a major contribution to this process.

There is a danger that in the quest for improvement in a particular sport the elements of one's training programme become separate and therefore detached from the actual sport. So weights are for strength and distance running is for endurance etc., each pursued without sufficient recognition that the training is, or should be, aimed at producing a better performance in the sport. Getting strong will only help a sports performance if the strength obtained is expressible in the sport. Equally the other elements of fitness can be at a good level but not being made available to the performance.

Skill training should be one unifying factor where all these separate elements are modelled into a practical whole. Flexibility is a fitness factor which although it needs work for its own sake must also become usable in the performance of the sport. Unlike the other elements of training, however, flexibility also has a fundamental unifying role because it essentially complements the other factors. You can be strong without being flexible but if you can be both the performance is enhanced. Equally relaxation and mental practices have a significant association with the

methodology of stretching, and so too does training for speed and endurance.

In the past, certainly in Great Britain, flexibility has been the Cinderella fitness factor, always last to be considered, if considered at all. It may also be the case in other countries that it has tended to have a lower rather than higher position in the rank order of importance. This needs to be put right because flexibility is just too important to be ignored.

Of course, in some sports like gymnastics, flexibility has always been recognized as crucial, but even here the reconciliation of improved flexibility with the strength and speed elements has not always been safe or efficient. Taking gymnastics as an example, it is worth noting how keen the coaches seem to be at measuring flexibility. This does indicate the value they put on it, but as discussed at the end of this chapter there are serious limitations to this approach.

Two other aspects of flexibility and flexibility training are fascinating as they somehow show up the essential peculiarity of flexibility; one at least may also shed some light on why flexibility work is less appealing to some sports performers. First, unlike any of the other aspects of fitness, flexibility is given to us in overabundance when we are born, but we steadily lose it. So the long-term strategy should not have to be flexibility development but flexibility maintenance. Second, there is an important anti-sport aspect to flexibility training. While you are doing it, to do it well you must be quiet, introverted and non-competitive, you must do it slowly and take a lot of time. Now, how does that fit the stereotype sportsman? Perhaps it fits the female type of socialization better and, if so, is that why women are generally more flexible than men?

TRAINING PRINCIPLES

Exercise or sport scientists have identified a number of principles of training (e.g. McArdle et al. 1981), and although they may argue about the full list, there are at least a few they all seem to agree about. As this chapter is concerned mainly with training it might be useful to summarize these principles:

REVERSIBILITY OR DETRAINING

Improvements in fitness factors gained through training are reversible. So strength increments gained by weights programmes and levels of endurance gained by steady running etc., are lost during extended periods of inactivity.

To some extent the easier the gains were to make the quicker they seem to be to lose, or put another way fitness improvements like those made in flexibility are much more persistent than, say, strength which is quicker to gain and lose.

Rest days are not periods of decline, however, but important parts of training in which the body adapts to the training rigours. Without rest days training will be less efficient and may even become redundant.

Detraining will be associated with periods of lay-off through illness, injury, holidays and changes in routine, even periods of competition, but can be offset by thoughtful manipulation of your regime. For example, a broken leg could mean a total rest for ten weeks and a lot of detraining, but all the top part of the body could still be training (in a modified way) and this will offset the effects. This can be thought of as *relative rest*. Innovative coaches and athletes will always look for ways of limiting the effect of layoff through modified training.

OVERLOAD

Improvements in fitness tend to come in smaller and smaller increments the fitter you get, but they all require overload to be achieved. In essence, this means that to initiate the biological changes or adaptations, the system being trained must be worked continuously near to its limit. This sets up the process of adaptation so that eventually the limit is extended. The time scale for change depends on the characteristics of the system, the original level of fitness, and the individual genetic and psychological characteristics. It is *not* always related to simply more time spent doing it.

Often, the problem is getting the level of overload right: too much and you over-use and then damage the system, too little and training is minimal. In flexibility it is very difficult to abuse the system if the right technique is used.

INDIVIDUAL DIFFERENCES

Sports magazines are very keen on showing their readers the training regimes of current élite performers with the hidden suggestion that if we did what they did we might be as good.

The principle of individual differences tells us this is a naïve belief. Programmes of training must be set up for you and not be off-the-shelf versions of someone else's. For example, there is the good marathon runner who needs to train between 80 to 110 miles a week, and in the same squad there may be another comparable runner who needs to do less than 50 miles to achieve her best fitness. Both are right and they reflect a mature and sensible understanding of individual differences.

SPECIFICITY

Finally, training must be directed at the requirements of the sport. Although you could gain aerobic fitness from cycling and this might be an enjoyable alternative for the swimmer, it will not be specific enough to substitute for endurance swimming. Equally, moving weights might exercise the same muscles used in the chosen sport, but are they moving in the same way, at the same speeds, etc.?

Static flexibility exercises are not the movements of the sport although they may and should mimic them closely. The dynamic sporting use of flexibility must accompany the static training to make the gains functionally useful.

RANGE OF MOTION (ROM)

Keeping in mind the principles above, in particular the last one, it is time to look at ROM and its constituent parts in order to be able to actually identify your requirements.

When reading about flexibility you will find terms like 'active' and 'passive', 'dynamic' and 'static' being used. It is important to be clear about these terms otherwise your training may be vague and the processes undertaken arbitrary. You would be breaking the training principles and achieving less than you should.

The principle of 'specificity' is an important one in all training, including flexibility training. Your training should reflect the specific needs of your sport, although it may also need to go further than just the sport specific requirements if it is to be safe and balanced. Everyone has an active range of motion for each joint and this should ideally match the skill requirements of your sport. This is the range over which you have voluntary muscular control. You also have passive ranges of motion, which are greater than the active ranges, and allow assisted extensions to an active movement without damage. Flexibility training should reflect both the need for active and passive ranges of motion.

Active and passive flexibility can be identified, and active and passive methods of stretching can be used to train them. However, in most circumstances the method of slow and static stretching (SASS) is preferred. This is basically a passive stretch under the control of the subject.

Dynamic and static flexibility are terms which describe, respectively, the actively produced range (sporting context) and the passively produced range of motion available. (*See also* Jenkins (1990) for complete definitions.) Dynamic flexibility is closest to active flexibility and is best thought of as the range of motion used in an activity mainly under the control of the muscles – although often incorporating the use of momentum built up by the activity, to extend the pure active flexibility range. If you like it is the 'real' situation. Static flexibility or extent flexibility can still be under control (but not necessarily yours) if achieved slowly. It tends to be applied to simple single movements and represents the element of flexibility that is most often measured by tests of flexibility.

The flexibility of a muscle or group of muscles cannot usefully be thought of in isolation from the opposing set of muscles. In the active situation, when one set of muscles is stretching, then it is the other set that is stretching them. So strengthening of the agonists is fundamental to achieving useful flexibility in the antagonists.

The other question to be thought through, of course, is whether a muscle in a stretched out position can still produce useful tension. Here we are talking about the strength of the antagonist when it switches to being the agonist. The answer is, again, strength training, but using the full range of movement so there is strengthening at the extremes of the muscle stretch. Indeed, as we will see, isometric contractions are used during some stretching techniques to enhance this. But in general terms the thing to be certain about is that full range movements are actively trained to build useful strength through all of the range from the most stretched out to the least.

We know that the range of motion available at any particular joint will normally be limited by the flexibility of the muscular components acting in the region. But this picture is too simplistic because the range of motion available will depend on whether the force creating the movement has been applied by the person using his own muscles alone, his own muscles plus an outside agency (gravity, body weight, another person's muscles) or just an outside agency. When the range achieved is purely through the subject's muscular activity it is an 'active' situation. When the impulse is completely from an outside agent then it is a 'passive' one.

In 'dynamic' sporting situations you will use active and passive ranges of flexibility and also some undefined combined active range with passive assistance. Only when the whole movement is under active muscular control can you be certain that damage will be avoided. Once the movement moves into the passive range then you must rely on the tissues' physical condition being adequate to sustain the rest of the movement without damage.

Two points to note are that:
a. The bigger the active range the better the control that can be established at the extremes of any movement.
b. The bigger the passive range the better the buffer zone between loss of active control and the onset of tissue damage.

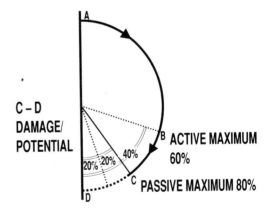

RANGE OF JOINT MOTION

The diagram above indicates these ranges in the 'typical' joint. If the theoretical range of motion in this joint is 180 degrees, then this represents 100 per cent of potential joint movement, and a–c represents the passive maximum of 80 per cent (144°). This leaves 20 per cent where damage will take place if the force applied pushes movement past the passive maximum. This 20 per cent also contains any as yet untouched potential for increasing passive flexibility. When the movement is an active one the range of movement in this example is reduced to 60 per cent as shown between a and b on the diagram. 40 per cent of the theoretical range is unachievable by unaided voluntary means.

Training needs to maintain and extend the active and passive ranges. The active range is more associated with strength while the passive is associated with tissue extensibility. The form of stretching used to achieve better active and passive ranges of flexibility should be SASS (or SASS plus PNF) but it needs to be associated with a strengthening programme designed to use the flexibility gained through training.

The active flexibility limit of a muscle such as the hamstrings, therefore, might be related to either the strength of the quadriceps or the passive flexibility of the hamstrings. If the quadriceps are too weak to pull out the hamstrings then the effective range of activity is reduced. If the internal resistance in the hamstrings is too high, again the active range is impaired.

SPEED, STRENGTH AND PLYOMETRICS

Muscles that are stretched offer less resistance to movement and require less energy for the movement to be executed. This suggests improvement in speed and indeed a more efficient use of stored energy reserves. The effect of flexibility training on speed has been investigated by Dintiman (1964) who studied the effect of different sprint training programmes on the running speed in a 50-yard sprint. It was found that the programme that included stretching and weight training resulted in a significant improvement in running speed when compared to an unsupplemented training programme. However, a programme of stretching without weight training or weight training without stretching did not lead to such results. The implication must be that a programme should be designed to include both these elements.

As you increase the range of motion (through your dedicated, specific, flexibility training) that you can call upon, you should use the muscles at these newly created limits, otherwise the flexibility gains will not be fulfilling their potential. In simple terms make sure you **actively** use your new range of motion. This may take a variety of forms in skill training and weight training. The thing to remember is take every movement of the weights you use through the whole of the possible joint motion.

There seem to be two relevant points to be made here. First, the effect of stretching exercises on strength, and second, the effect of strength on flexibility. With regard to the first point, the evidence is that flexibility development does not lead to any reduction in strength. O'Connell (1960) found no significant differences in strength after subjects performed six weeks of controlled stretching. It can also be seen just from observation that good gymnasts do not lack strength, even though they develop extreme ranges of motion in their joints.

With regard to the second point, the effect of strength exercises on flexibility, there are still coaches who dislike weight training because they believe that athletes will become 'muscle bound' and then their flexibility will consequently suffer. This is a myth; if weight training exercises are performed correctly through the full range of motion, flexibility will not be hindered. The overall extra bulk of muscle may slightly limit some movement patterns in extreme cases, but this does not mean that in general terms weight training need reduce flexibility. An all-round weight training programme is required so that all movements specific to a sports skill are exercised. This needs to be combined with an equivalent flexibility programme. Massey and Chaudet (1957) found that the only measure of flexibility that was significantly less after a weight training schedule, was the subject's ability to hyperextend the arms at the shoulder joint. This was because no flexibility exercise had been included for such a movement.

Morehouse and Rasch (1958) stated:

It is now generally accepted that an individual becomes muscle bound only when he consistently exercises one muscle or group of muscles in a fixed position which does not permit a complete range of motion, with the result that connective tissue in the muscles becomes adapted to this position and becomes shortened.

As this was published over thirty years ago we really should have had time to come to terms with it! Some of the very biggest and strongest women and men who consistently use heavy weights in their training have shown very good flexibility – because they train hard for that aspect as well. Indeed, the more weights you do the more flexibility training should be incorporated. There are of course those who just want to pose and not really use their muscles in real sport. They may find that the opposite strategy of heavy weights, restricted movements and little flexibility work suits their needs. Returning to proper sport and sensible training it is clear that flexibility and strength are not only compatible but essential training bedfellows.

Thus it can be seen that it is important to perform weight-training exercises through the full range of motion of the joint. Athletes using weights in general, and, in particular, those using multi-gym type apparatus, should check that the apparatus does not hinder this. Often the full range of motion may well not be utilized e.g. during some knee extension exercises. Although this may be for good safety reasons with very heavy weights on the leg press*, it should not mean that full extension is ignored. This is particularly relevant as an example, because full extension is not naturally used in many sports like cycling and running. It must, however, be included in training to achieve muscle balance: another exercise should be introduced so the final aspect of extension can be trained.

In this case, the medial quadricep muscle is in question and is important in maintaining proper patella position relative to the femoral groove; imbalance here between the various aspects of the quadricep muscle group is considered a major contribution to chronic knee pains like Chondromalacia patellae. So we have a good case for training a muscle that seems at first sight less important in the actions of the sport, but is really crucial for maintaining freedom from injury.

One should be aware that set pieces of apparatus like multi-gyms can restrict the

*Leg-press exercises if locked out with heavy weights attached may seriously damage the patella as the force acting back in this position is not being supported through the muscle because of the full extension alignment of the limbs.

range of motion, in some cases by their dimensions alone and/or their dimensions relative to the size of the user. Equally any apparatus may be used restrictively by the operator. The test is simple: try the movement with no weight attached. Then ask yourself if you could have gone further than you did while still maintaining the correct form. If the answer is 'yes' then you are not using the full range. Remember what was said in the physiology section about strength/length curves. The most ineffective muscle pull will be at the extremes of the joint's possible motion, therefore, the weight attached may well have to be considerably lighter than it would for the more mechanically advantageous positions. Good multi-gym type apparatus has some inbuilt mechanism for increasing the weight applied as the movement proceeds.

You should be clear on your objectives in doing the strength training. Here the objective is to increase the strength at the newly acquired limits of flexibility and therefore you need to be sure you will be applying weights to the fibres at their longest. It does not matter if the lifts become easy after the initial part because it is the extreme position we are trying to strengthen, so that the range of motion becomes actually actively useful. This sort of strength training does not always have to include any actual weights because, at least initially, the weight of the limb or body segment may well be more than enough.

Finally, plyometrics needs to be considered. Plyometrics usually takes the form of depth jumping and should not be confused with flexibility training. It is a special form of training which aims to increase explosive power; power being the product of strength and speed. The theory behind its practice is as follows. A concentric (shortening) contraction is much stronger if it immediately follows an eccentric contraction (lengthening or pre-stretching of the same muscle). The more a muscle is pre-stretched before a concentric contraction occurs, the greater the force the muscle will be able to exert. In depth jumping, the athlete may jump off a high box then rebound off the floor onto another (usually lower) box. The pre-stretching of the muscles as the athlete descends from the first box causes the muscle to resist overstretching by stimulating the muscle spindle. Thus the stretch reflex is invoked and a powerful contraction results preventing the muscle from overstretching, so the athlete can rebound from the floor with greater power. However, plyometrics carries the dangers of ballistic stretches, and the forces exerted at the knee joint, for example, can cause damage to ligaments and other tissues. Plyometrics should therefore be treated with caution. In addition, at least some people are less than convinced of its usefulness: 'there has not been strong evidence for its effectiveness in improving performances in sport.' (Jenkins 1990)

ENDURANCE, AEROBICS AND MOVEMENT WITH MUSIC

By its nature, endurance is concerned with repetition at sub-maximal levels and it would appear that the nature of these repetitions can be associated with a considerably higher percentage of chronic injury than non-endurance sports. Intrinsic tissue resistance to movement will in the long term be just as debilitating as it is in the more spectacular acute injury situation.

The combination of stretching programmes and endurance activities should be just as natural a part of training for the endurance athlete as flexibility and strength training is for the power performer.

A popular modern form of endurance activity is what has generically been called 'aerobics'. Aerobics as a term in common sports usage is often a misnomer when you look at it in practice. It should be about endurance training for cardiovascular fitness, but often it can be so intense it becomes more of an anaerobic or 'sprint' type activity than an aerobic one.

Another consideration is the type of movements employed and the music or beat which accompany them. There are some movements in 'aerobics' classes which give cause for concern. Many ballistic movements take place and thus many individuals are likely to perform bouncing, a type of stretching not recommend. By this I mean that a series of swinging type movements are initiated and then allowed to become or stay 'passive'. Thus, the limb or body part has lost the control otherwise exerted by active muscle actions, and the brake is only applied by the soft tissue absorbing the generated forces around the joints.

In a group situation, people are inclined to 'go a bit too far', and the presence of music can aggravate this. Before an 'aerobics' class, just like before any activity, static stretching should be done after a general warm-up (which for 'aerobics' could take the form of jogging, or dancing, but without stressful movements). The body will then be better equipped to tolerate the stressful ballistic movements that seem inevitably to take place in many 'aerobics' classes.

The effects of music on exercise need more research, but it can be postulated that music, especially the heavy fast-beat type often favoured in 'aerobics' classes, may alter an individual's perception and threshold of pain. Music does have advantages with regard to motivation and creating a good atmosphere, but should be thought of as a background to, rather than the stimulus for, movement. When performing repetitive or rhythmical exercises, many individuals find music beneficial, but care should be taken particularly when performing ballistic movements or, for example, a near maximum continuous force movement with weights.

BREATHING RANGE

By simply taking measurements of body circumferences at three levels, abdomen, diaphragm, chest, at full exhalation and inhalation one can get three numerical values for the range of breathing. Prichard (1987) quotes élite swimmers as having results of 2½ to 3 (or even 4) inches at each point.

Seemingly for swimmers, and arguably for many other sports performers too, a restriction in this breathing range is a significant limitation to potential. We have here another example of how stretching muscles not related to the primary movements of the sport can in effect enhance the performance. All the major muscles of the trunk (back and chest) should be stretched to assist the breathing potential.

The more fully the lungs can expand and thus fill with air and the more completely they can empty, the more efficiently can the internal environment of blood and muscles be oxygenated. Thus flexibility can be seen to have a direct relationship to the biochemistry of muscle function.

Prichard, in his case studies on swimmers, presents impressive figures showing immediate improvements in split times associated with releasing connective tissue adhesions which were restricting the breathing range. The build-up of such adhesions were not released by stretching, but by more aggressive therapy. However, had the swimmers previously put as much time and effort into their flexibility as their strength work, the adhesions could have been avoided. His recommendation for 'tight' swimmers is to spend as much time stretching as they do in training strength. This is very sensible advice for other groups of sports performers as well.

RELAXATION AND MENTAL TRAINING

Like many terms used both colloquially and technically there is often some problem in squaring up the common usage with the specific meaning. For example, some first-year undergraduate students have problems with words like 'fitness' and 'health' because of the preconceptions common usage gives them. 'Relaxation' falls into the same category of words and should therefore be treated with a little care.

In the context of this book on flexibility a clear understanding of what is meant technically by the term relaxation is important to the reader but much more important will be the reader's ability to learn the skill of relaxation as it applies to stretching.

From everyday use the image of flopping down in an armchair might be your vision of being relaxed. This has the associated sense of shutting down the brain, not working and taking pleasure in being non-productive. In the sporting (and stretching) context, however, the cultivation of the muscular aspects of 'flopping' and its application to specific muscles is relevant, but the associated mental dullness of the armchair definition is most definitely not wanted.

Productivity in sport and flexibility is enhanced through the ability to target muscles for working and muscles for relaxing. In the active situation the unskilled player uses more muscular effort to achieve this end than the skilled player will need to use. Additionally, that end product will be less adequate and, nearly always, noticeably less smooth and flowing. The image you might wish to conjure up is, say, a ballet dancer moving effortlessly across the stage or a Russian gymnast working a routine on the parallel bars. Then mentally compare this with how you or an untrained and poorly co-ordinated friend might look attempting the same sequences.

Relaxation of muscles not needed in a movement is a sign of real skill and allows energy stores to be used economically. Compare if you will the early finishers in the London marathon with the later arrivals. All the runners have covered the same distance, some in about two hours and others in five or six hours. Who of these have managed to use their energy stores most efficiently? Those who glide over the ground at a steady (high) pace, with heads still and arms moving rhythmically, are using most of their energy for propulsion – they are energy misers, wasting nothing. The slower runners may start with the same reserves of energy but spend it frivolously on rolling heads, irratic pace and wobbling bodies.

So relaxation for our purposes applies

to a state of affairs in the muscles. But it is a learnt skill and needs to be trained so that it can be turned on at will. Thus there is most definitely a mental aspect to relaxation; so we often talk of 'relaxed concentration' and 'feeling the state of your muscles', which implies an active mental process.

Clearly the ability to be relaxed can be interfered with by other things such as competition, for example. Performances are sometimes difficult to produce under tournament conditions because the ability to relax has been impaired by some mental anxiety associated with the competitive situation. Skills which were routine, flowing and confident may become jerky, harassed and unsuccessful. Learnt behaviours like passing, throwing and kicking seem to lose their automatic nature as higher centres of the brain start to interfere.

Thus I think we can identify at least two strands to relaxation of importance here. First, there is the ability to relax a muscle or set of muscles for training and performance purposes, and second, there must be the control of that relaxation under externally or internally applied pressure.

As far as flexibility work is concerned directly, it is necessary to be involved with the first of these strands. But through the practice of relaxation for stretching we will help to train the second aspect as well.

This second, mental training, aspect is a major concern of modern sports psychology because however good the physical training the ability to express that training in competition is the key to success – and that comes down to mental abilities as often as not.

It also helps to explain why seemingly poorly trained (physically) performers produce results in sport above expectations and conversely why great physically conditioned athletes may underachieve. The really top-class athletes might be defined in terms of their combined abilities relating to both mental and physical expression of skills.

RELAXATION METHODS

Alter (1988) suggests that all relaxation methods fall into three categories:
1. The use of special stretching techniques;
2. The use of special modalities, drugs or aids;
3. The use of mind-controlling techniques; but in practical terms one can use combinations of elements of these categories to enhance the ability to relax.

It is also true to say there is a circularity to these methods: by practising mental techniques you improve your ability to relax muscles and so can stretch more efficiently – but by stretching you also enhance muscle relaxation and put the mind in a more receptive state for relaxation to occur (less internal tension).

Overlay on this the environmental factors (under 2 above) and you start to build one practical and functional regime for relaxation. Heat, for example, has been used as a 'modality' for tension reduction for a long time and in many different ways. Saunas, warm baths, jacuzzis, thermal mud applications all use heat to enhance relaxation.

In trying to relax to allow stretching to be as efficient as possible, one needs to create the appropriate environment and by doing so one will enhance the process of gaining mental control over the muscles which will have application in the performance of the chosen sport. Once achieved a relaxed state can be used both for efficient stretching and for mental practice such as thinking through the strategies and movements for sport. The stretching helping the relaxation and the mental imagery aiding the sport.

It is not a remit of this text to go into the details of mental practices which are the reserve of sports psychology but for those who want to look further into these areas there are several references in the bibliography.

The following is a suggested strategy for relaxation appropriate to stretching for flexibility.

1. *Environment*. Choose as warm and where possible as comfortable a situation in which to stretch. All extraneous aggravations to relaxation, such as restrictive clothing, noise, etc., should be avoided.

If you find gentle massage helps as a preliminary to stretching, then use it as it will not do any harm and if you like it you will relax all the better.

2. *Breathing*. Start the process by becoming aware of your own breathing and try to increase the depth of each breath a little and decrease the number or rate a little. To this end it is recommended you just hold the IN and the OUT position for a couple of seconds before emptying and refilling lungs respectively, but only breathe like this for about five breaths before returning to a light slow normal breathing pattern.

When the rhythm is established try to maintain it through the exercises and if tension starts to return then re-establish relaxation by doing the deep slow method again. As you breathe out, feel the tension flow away from your muscles. The stretch

when it comes should be associated with the exhalation part as this is the relaxation phase. So the slowness of the stretch is associated with sequential exhalations.

3. *Concentration*. Throughout a stretching sequence you should be mentally checking the state of tension in your muscles. All unnecessary tension should be avoided so it is best to use stretches in which there is maximum body support from outside, i.e. the floor or a chair. It is recognized that it is not always possible to stretch some muscles from this ideal, passively supported position, but it should be the aim to gain as much assistance as possible.

As a device to assist in the process you might develop a particular mental image, for example, letting your muscles become liquid or letting waves at the sunny seashore roll over you. You can achieve, with practice, a very detached floating feeling over which you have complete control and in which your target muscles are more fully and easily stretched.

4. *SASS*. This is simply applying the slow and static stretches which are recommended and described in this text. As the muscle is pulled out, so resistance will naturally increase and so physiological processes come into play as described in the section on neurophysiological factors in Chapter 3. During the process, relaxation is enhanced and a further stretch is desirable and possible.

FLEXIBILITY ASSESSMENT

Although at first glance this may seem a strange heading in a chapter about the relationships between flexibility and other forms of training, it is in fact most relevant. This is so because assessment and measurement are used as training stimulants and for selection criteria in many sports. Also people like to know how their training is going.

It is possible to measure flexibility directly by means of goniometry, electro-goniometry, radiography and using a Leighton flexiometer. But indirect measures of distances are practically popular outside the laboratory (Hubley, 1982).

Many coaches like to use flexibility tests to 'show' improvement, aid the athlete's motivation and give an objective feedback value on some of the decisions that must be made about selection, performance, changes in training programme, etc. Unfortunately the tests may give an inaccurate and relatively arbitrary set of values if not conducted correctly.

'Flexibility testing' can tend to increase competition between the individuals being tested, thus encouraging them to use unsafe techniques to achieve a better score; for example, if the splits is being used as a estimate of flexibility, by jerking downwards a wide spread may be achieved, thus giving a high score. However, damage is likely to be done, and so such testing can be rather counter-productive in the long run. Certainly good supervision is needed to get anything at all worthwhile out of flexibility assessment – and even with this supervision it is debatable whether it is any good!

The essence of good flexibility work is slow, relaxed, gentle movements followed by relaxed holding of positions – this is true in PNF as well as in the basic technique. As soon as you introduce assessment, relaxation becomes more difficult to maintain and results may not, therefore, reflect flexibility as much as tension.

There are plenty of other variables which may affect the assessment, making it very difficult to control:

1. The warmth of an athlete's muscles can affect the results obtained and it is not possible to be certain that each individual is equally well warmed up at the time of assessment, nor as warm or warmer at any retest with which you require comparison. External environmental conditions will also be an important thermal variable.

2. The level of previous muscle activity will affect results, because exercise always creates some degree of fatigue and this in turn stimulates an unpredictable level of tension in the muscles.

3. Flexibility assessment at one or two sites cannot be assumed to be true for other sites, so a selection of sites will have to be tested. In addition, cooling off during the process may affect the objectivity of the tests.

4. The flexibilities which coaches are going to measure will be in more complex joints, that is, back, shoulders and hips. Therefore, it becomes difficult to isolate the relevant movements and accurately repeat the methods.

5. Static measures as obtained by most flexibility tests may not in fact relate to dynamic situations relevant to sport. The majority of tests are aimed at measuring static flexibility, whereas flexibility in sport is mainly dynamic.

It must be remembered that the important coaching quality is to know (theoretically and practically) how to improve an athlete's flexibility towards optimum in a safe, usable way and to teach the techniques which will call on that reserve of flexibility.

Probably the most significant assessment is to make subjective (but informed) judgements as to the location of tensions and restrictions in the movements of athletes by using clear observations, assisted where possible and necessary by experienced and qualified observers of movement (sports physiotherapists, paediatrists, physical educationalists, etc.). This will identify areas that need more attention and then programmes can be devised to work on these areas.

However, whatever is said against them, it is certain that some people will want tests. If the coach uses them with great care and recognizes the major reservations outlined above, there *may* be a place for them.

A GUIDE TO MEASURING FLEXIBILITY

1. Use a set warm-up procedure related to the areas to be tested. Always use the same procedure.
2. Use as constant an environment as possible and keep the same conditions for retesting.
3. Make sure athletes are dressed in the same way, for example, no shoes, loose clothing, etc.
4. Measure each individual alone because the presence of others implies competition and affects motivation.
5. Do not impart results (his/hers or others) to the athlete during the measurement.
6. Try to measure athletes at the same time of day, after the same sort of previous forty-eight hours in terms of activity, travel, etc.
7. Use tests which work without gravitational assistance, for example, sit and reach rather than touch toes from standing.
8. Use static and dynamic tests.

9. Repeat the tests three times with a set period for rest between.
10. Use ranges rather than centimetres, i.e. from 5 to 10 rather than 5.2 cms.
11. Do not just use tests – observe as well.

TYPICAL TESTS OF STATIC FLEXIBILITY

1. Shoulder hyperextension

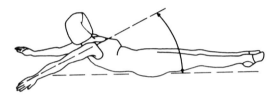

2. Hamstring/lower back flexibility

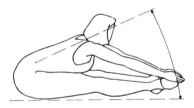

3. Shoulder hyperextension

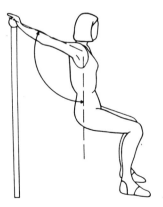

4. Shoulder hyperflexion

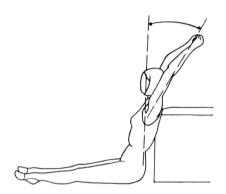

5. Side splits stretch

6. Front splits stretch

7. Hip extension

8. Active hip extension

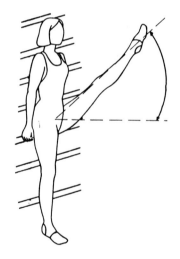

(Illustrations reproduced by courtesy of the National Coaching Foundation)

TYPICAL TESTS OF DYNAMIC FLEXIBILITY

For dynamic flexibility you need to arrange repetitions of activities which are close to movements seen in your sport and measure the speed of completion and/or observe the range of motion achieved.

In squash, for example, you might use a modified shuttle run in which the subject was timed over a set course round the court, including regular lunges to touch the walls with the racket. The better the dynamic flexibility the quicker the completion because less ground would need to be covered by the flexible player who could stretch further. Obviously the taller player has more natural reach but if the scores are just used to compare the player with himself the test can be useful.

Modifications of this type of idea can be made for many skills in many speed-related sports. Tests must be thought of as separate from training and used sparingly and with accuracy of measurement in mind.

Gym tests like star jumps or squat thrusts per minute, obstacle runs, etc., combine a measure of dynamic flexibility with other aspects of fitness like explosive strength and endurance and may be useful as well.

REFERENCES

Albinson, J. G. and Bull, S. J., *A Mental Game Plan*, Spondyn, 1988

Alter, M. J., *Science of Stretching*, Human Kinetics, 1988

Bull, S. J., 'Personal and situational influences on adherence to mental skills training', paper given at the British Association of Sports Sciences conference, September 13–15, 1990

Dintiman, G. B., 'Effect of various training programs on running speed', *Research Quarterly* 35, pp456–63, 1964

Greipp, J. F., 'Swimmer's Shoulder: The Influence of Flexibility and Weight Training', *Physician and Sports-medicine* 13(8): pp92–105, 1985

Hubley, C., 'Testing Flexibility', *Physiological Testing of the Elite Athlete*, edited by MacDougall, J. D., Wenger, M. A., Green, H. J., pp117–32, Movement (New York), 1982

Jenkins, S. P. R., *Sports Science Handbook*, Sunningdale, 1990

Massey, B. A. and Chaudet, N. L., 'Effects of Systematic, Heavy Resistance Exercise on Range of Joint Movement in Young Male Adults, *Research Quarterly* 27(1): pp41–51, 1956

McArdle, W., Katch, F. and Katch, V., *Exercise Physiology: Energy, Nutrition, and Human Performance*, Lea and Febiger (Philadelphia), 1986

McNaught-Davis, J. P., *Developing Flexibility* (Resource Pack), National Coaching Foundation, 1986

McNaught-Davis, J. P., *Developing Flexibility* (Video), Brighton Polytechnic, Media Services, Watts Bld., Brighton

Morehouse, L. E. and Rasch, P. J., *Scientific Basis of all Training*, W. B. Saunders, 1958

Prichard, B., 'Increasing Your Range', *Swimming Technique*, pp7–10, Feb–Apr. 1987

Prichard, B., 'Stretching for Speed', *Swimming Technique*, pp 32–6 May–July 1987

Terry, P., *The Winning Mind*, Thorsons, 1989

PART TWO

THE STRETCHING MANUAL

6

STRETCHING METHODS (SASS)

The importance of flexibility training in its own right cannot be denied, but through good flexibility work the athlete can release more of his other trained attributes in competition and performance and with much less risk of injury. So the expression of strength, endurance, speed and skill within the sporting performance will be enhanced through flexibility work.

Up to this point, therefore, the thrust of my text has been a set of arguments, based on theory and practice of sport, but with limited direct practical advice on how to train for flexibility: Part Two redresses that balance.

If Part One has been the physical and chemical laws of relevance to the internal combustion engine then Part Two is the driver's manual and the driving lessons.

There are in essence only three ways to stretch, one is always right, one may sometimes be right but is usually unnecessary and one is always wrong. These are looked at in the next four chapters. The point of including a 'wrong' method is for recognition rather than practice because it can easily masquerade as or infiltrate into the two acceptable forms of stretching. Whichever of the acceptable methods you will be using there will be in this form of training (like in any other) a need to prepare. The theoretical benefits of warm-up have been mentioned but the procedures have not, so they are dealt with in this chapter as is the whole mechanics of slow and static stretching (SASS) and creating a work programme. The advanced and ballistic stretches have a chapter to themselves as do the specific stretches for sports.

GUIDELINES FOR STRETCHING

Slow and static stretching (SASS) is the best method to improve flexibility and thus forms the basis of muscle conditioning for all sports. This premise is based on anatomical and physiological evidence together with the sport medical opinion and research data available, and already discussed.

SASS involves holding a muscle in a maximal position of stretch. The length of time allowed is recommended variously to be between 10–60 seconds. However, the evidence put forward by Borms et al. 1987 finds no reason for this to go beyond 10 (8–15) seconds compared to 20 or 30 seconds.

There are, however, according to Anderson two distinct parts to a full stretch and this is based on the interplay between the stretch and inverse stretch reflexes discussed in Chapter 3.

The initial or primary stretch is held for 10 seconds and followed by a further

stretch, as the muscle relaxes a little, to a new maximum or full stretch. This final position should be held for a while but without pain or loss of form. When you are new to stretching this should be about 10 seconds. Maybe later, as you get more relaxed and confident, 30 seconds will be possible. This type of training should not be thought of as competitive or even the same from day to day. Take as long or as short a time as you can while staying relaxed and concentrating.

As mentioned above, research into this matter has not shown that a particular amount of time is most effective in the development of flexibility. Beaulieu suggests that 30 seconds per stretch might be a suitable period; this seems a sensible

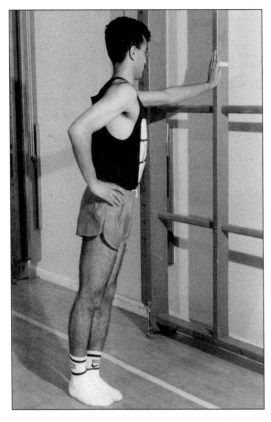

Every part of the stretch must be totally under control so you can stop the movement at any point with no momentum carrying it on – with a bounce you are losing control.

It is important to be clear about 'stretching to the point of resistance'. It is the fundamental difference between good and bad stretching. The following analogy will help to give the right idea:

Imagine you are trying to sneak into a building without being noticed. You have to open an old door with rusty hinges. You must open it slowly and smoothly, but when you start to feel resistance you must stop because a loud creak will draw the attention of the guards.

You can think of holding a stretch as being equivalent to an 'oiling process' that will enable the athlete to stretch that little bit further next time.

Pain is an indication of tissue damage – pain is not a part of this sort of training.

It is also important that you release slowly from the stretch. You must aim to relax the muscles as they are being stretched and learn to find and control the right amount of stretch. By 'right amount of stretch' I mean what feels right, and it will vary from day to day, but this is quite normal and the variation can be ignored. Never expect each session to produce an improvement.

The importance of correct alignment of the lower back, head and shoulders and the legs during the different exercises needs to be stressed. Without this alignment you may pull too much on ligaments instead of through the muscle. In later sections there are plenty of stretches that are all explained with photographs so that alignments and positions can be checked.

amount to build towards, and although people will differ, a general aim to increase the time to about 30 seconds is recommended. The most important thing is to hold a stretch long enough for the natural relaxation of the inverse stretch reflex to take place, that is, for more than 6 seconds and for perhaps 10 seconds to be sure. At this point a new maximum stretch can be achieved . . . with practice.

You should passively stretch the muscle to the point of resistance which is before you feel pain. This must be a very slow process to be sure that you only reach 'resistance' and that there is no elastic recoil or jerkiness. If you bounce there is an obvious rebound, which is both ineffective and dangerous and must be avoided.

It is suggested that in a stretching routine, three or four sets of each exercise, held for up to 30 seconds each time, could be the eventual aim, although this will take a while to achieve. Notwithstanding, only a couple of stretches will be sufficient to maintain a steady improvement. All the stretches should feel easy and not painful however many repeats you do. Going for 'burns' or 'maximums' is just dangerous, uninformed and counter-productive.

Both sides of your body must be equally stretched (for example, right leg and left leg). The concept of balance has been mentioned already and is important. The only reason to favour one set of muscles on one side of the body over the other would be a remedial one. If after years of neglect or injury your range of motion has been restricted unevenly then a remedial programme of stretching may favour the affected areas. This would not normally mean not stretching the 'good' ones, but rather, stretching the restricted ones more. You may well be aware of such imbalances and may decide to institute your own remedial programme, however, there are experts in the field of remedial therapy so some advice might be sensible and worthwhile.

Keep in mind the importance of warming up before stretching (see end of chapter) – on some occasions warm-up exercises may well have to be interspersed with the stretching so the body does not cool down. As the biophysical factors indicated in Chapter 3, being very warm or even hot is a prerequisite to stretching. Thus flexibility training placed after activity is a particularly good strategy. You will hopefully be very hot, very tired and in a relaxed frame of mind at this time. Stretching also aids the recovery processes making muscle stiffness less likely (*see* de Vries, 1962).

One must also realize that gains in flexibility come gradually and improvements may only be realized over months rather than weeks. Ideally daily stretching sessions are needed for significant improvement. This may seem impossible in a busy schedule but there are plenty of ways of stretching while doing other things and there are some ideas for this later.

There seems to be no evidence that it is possible to overtrain for flexibility – **as long as the method is SASS and it is correctly performed**. Flexibility like any other sort of fitness attribute will decline if stretching training ceases, though the effects of flexibility training are quite persistent in comparison to increases in other fitness attributes like strength, for example.

It is very important to make a clear distinction between warm-up/warm-down and training. Short bursts of static stretching as used by performers before and after a match, a competition or a training session are part of a process of warm-up or warm-down. Serious, planned sessions of proper static stretching constitute flexibility training. The aim of the former in the warm-up/warm-down is to be able to stretch to the present limitations of the body and help arouse the system for activity or relax from it. The main aim of stretching in flexibility training is to improve upon the present range of movement about joints. To achieve the latter a separate period dedicated to this is required within the wider training programme. No permanent changes in flexibility will accrue from warm-up or warm-down.

By all means use a couple of appropriate stretches to the point of resistance as a part of the warm-up and warm-down. Do not, however, interpret this as training flexibility.

During training you are taking much more time and working to the limit to achieve permanent increases in range of motion.

DEVELOPING A STRETCHING ROUTINE

There is a wide range of individual differences between people so not everyone can achieve the same level. But practice will help everyone although people often find it difficult to keep the practice going.

Adherence to training programmes is a serious concern of sports psychologists, and flexibility is one of the fitness factors most prone to being ignored and therefore not adhered to. There are ways, however, of helping athletes and yourself to comply with and adhere to stretching programmes. It is important to recognize that this form of training is not very exciting and needs to be 'marketed' to the athlete and yourself.

In the early days of introducing stretching to a squad or group you can learn together and observe each other co-operating to identify areas of weakness and strength. It is up to the coach to emphasize the non-competitive and relaxed nature of this training, so warm, friendly and comfortable environments are the order of the day. This can be seen as a bonus from hard exhausting exercise.

As the individuals learn the stretches and techniques they can become part of any situation where you can relax. So team talks, tactics sessions, reviewing match videos and half-time periods are all appropriate stretching times. If the coach sees it as important to relax and stretch then the players are more likely to adhere to the programme.

Encouraging the use of 'free' time for stretching during all aspects of the sports performer's day can easily build up a considerable total of training in flexibility. The coach and squad members will also notice the ones who do not train, or train in an unbalanced way, and can intervene. If all the training is left to individuals in their private time the coach may miss the player who is avoiding this aspect of his training, especially during the early days of learning how to do it and how important it is.

Flexibility for the individual who trains alone is more difficult to encourage. However, it is not so specific that individuals from different sports cannot help each other and, if associated with the pleasures of finishing a hard session, can be easier to maintain.

When developing your own programme take into account why you are trying to improve your flexibility, how flexible you are already (where your weaknesses are) and how much time you have to spend regularly on it. It is much better to spend 10 minutes every day than 70 minutes on one day a week. It is better to do one exercise well and completely at one sitting than to try to get through two or three incorrectly or quickly.

If a particular exercise cannot be achieved without pain or great effort then do not do it, choose another which stretches the same muscles. Come back to the first choice when you have improved. Conversely, if an exercise never gets a muscle to a point of resistance, look for a more advanced alternative.

Whenever you stretch and for whatever sport the principle of planning is the same. There are five steps to this planning, the first three having a specific question to be answered. The coach needs to ask these questions for each member of his squad and not just assume that everyone should do the same stretches.

STEP I: When can you do flexibility training? (Total time available. Times of day etc.)

STEP II: How many exercises do you need to do for your sport or sports? (General programme plus emphasis for sport/person.)

STEP III: How many days will cover one completion of your programme?

STEP IV: Make a plan of the order and times of exercises.

STEP V: Regularly change some of the exercises for alternatives.

TOTAL PROGRAMME – AN EXAMPLE OF ORGANIZATION

Some muscles are fairly small and the joints they work on are quite simple, and therefore one stretch will probably act on nearly all the fibres. Slight involuntary daily differences in the exercise will account for adequate stretching of those fibres which on other days may be missed.

However, many muscles are large and combine in their actions with other muscles. They may also work across two joints and/or be involved with more complicated joints. Thus, in order to be certain of stretching all the fibres in these muscles you need more than one stretch. It is not really accurate to see all stretches of, say, the hamstrings so much as alternatives doing the same job, but rather as ways of ensuring good coverage of all the tissue in that muscle group.

Sometimes you can just alter your position slightly within one specific stretch and thus move the pull to new fibres. Whatever you do the important thing is to be sure you are only stretching the muscle and associated fascia and obeying all the other simple rules like relaxation and gentle, slow, non-jerky movements.

When you start it is fine just to pick a few simple stretches and work on them for a few days but, as you get more confident, try to build up a repertoire of different stretches aimed at the same areas and then you will be more likely to do a really good job. As a practical example of the benefit of this approach just consider situations in, say, squash when you suddenly have to stretch your hamstrings; this could be in any one of a great variety of directions all of which would be pulling on slightly different fibres in the group. You will not have control over this; you will just react. Again you may just slip and stretch outside your normal active range; this too is unpredictable. If your stretching programme has been 'total' for the hamstrings you will be much more likely to withstand the stretch and not get injured. However, a limited programme in which you always stretch the hamstrings by a toe touch with legs together, might never really condition parts of the group and thus leave you much more vulnerable. The same story applies to non-sporting situations, such as missing a step on the stairs or slipping on the ice, the resultant sudden pull could tug on any fibres and they need to have been preconditioned by controlled stretch programmes of training in order to be able to come through undamaged. The programme must therefore be designed with this in mind.

It is actually (generally) false to suppose that a stretch will identify just one muscle; most of the stretches, like the one below, pull on more than just one area. It is often a convenience rather than a real sense of accuracy to call a stretch, for example, a 'hamstring' stretch.

If you have, say, a two-day stretch programme with nine stretches a day, and over that period you cover all the muscle groups, then the next two days could be repeating the programme but on each day substituting five of the stretches with alternative stretches. On the next two-day repeat you might exchange another five stretches, and then take a day off before starting the sequence again. This would be a balanced week's programme. See the table on p.71.

The idea of balance is important, not just in the total programme covering a good variety of slightly different pulls, but also in terms of symmetry from left to right and back to front. The programme you use should not favour one side over the other unless you are deliberately carrying out remedial action on one stiff

area. Simply, this balance can always be achieved by never doing one leg or arm or shoulder, etc., without following it with its pair. It is also sensible to switch the order every few weeks in case you tend to be, without knowing it, more enthusiastic to start with in a sequence, or at one time of the day.

Before moving on to Chapter 7 and looking at stretches, it is worth thinking about the practicality of fitting stretching into your day. This harps back to the problem of adherence; if you get a routine it tends

A REPEATING TWO-DAY PROGRAMME

S T R E T C H E S ----------->

	1	2	3	4	5	6	7	8	9
DAY 1	1	2	3	4	5	6	7	8	9
MON	A7	D1	B1	C1	B3	C4	B4	C8	E1
DAY 2	10	11	12	13	14	15	16	17	18
TUES	A1	D2	D4	C11	A3	C6	B7	C5	E2
DAY 1	1	2	3	4	5	6	7	8	9
WEDS	A5	D1	B2	C1	B5	C12	B4	C8	E3
DAY 2	10	11	12	13	14	15	16	17	18
THURS	A2	D2	D4	C3	A4	C6	B7	C9	E1
DAY 1	1	2	3	4	5	6	7	8	9
FRI	A5	D4	B2	C10	B5	C12	B6	C2	E2
DAY 2	10	11	12	13	14	15	16	17	18
SAT	A2	D3	D1	C3	A4	C7	B8	C9	E3
REST									
SUN	**NO STRETCHES** ------------->								
DAY 1	1	2	3	4	5	6	7	8	9
MON	A7	D1	B1	C1	B3	C4	B4	C8	E1
DAY 2	10	11	12	13	14	15	16	17	18
TUES	A1	D2	D4	C11	A3	C6	B7	C5	E2

KEY

Uppers
A1 Cat stretch
A2 Flat-cat stretch
A3 Tail-cat stretch
★ A4 Shoulder pull-down
★ A5 Shoulder pull-across
★ A6 Shoulder pull-up
★★ A7 Neck pull

Mid
B1 Flat-chest
B2 Towel chest
B3 Back roll
★ B4 Leg over
B5 Tuck
★ B6 Twister
★ B7 Volunter
★ B8 Straddle lean

Lowers
★ C1 Hams
★ C2 Knee chest
C3 Bottoms up
C4 Buddha
★ C5 Groin straddle
★ C6 Groin lunge
C7 Lying groin
★ C8 Chaise-longue
★ C9 Queueing
★ C10 Quadriceps lunge
★ C11 Achilles' heel
★ C12 Calf stretch
★ C13 Shin stretch

Extremities
★ D1 Ankle rotation
★ D2 Toes stretch
★ D3 Wrist rotation
D4 Fingers stretch

Totals
E1 Elongation
★★ E2 Straddle lean
★ E3 Standing side stretch

(★ left and right side repeats, ★★ combine a set of stretches)

Each one is 10 seconds primary followed by 20–30 seconds full stretch and repeated twice. With warm-ups about 45 mins/day. *See* Chapter 7 for desciptions of exercises.

to gather its own inertia. There really is an opportunity with this activity of slow careful stretching to use your time efficiently. Just consider how stretching could become part of your day.

STRETCHING EXERCISES AT HOME

In this section we see the home as the gymnasium. This does not mean that all dedicated sports people should ignore this section, as the quality of the flexibility training possible at home is just as good as, and maybe even better than, that which can be achieved in the sports hall or gymnasium.

ADVANTAGES

No one else need see you, therefore, it is easier to relax.

No one else to interfere, therefore, it is easier to relax.

No travel, no time additions, therefore, it is easier to relax.

Fit it in, around and during other activities, therefore, you make good use of time and it is easier to relax.

Free of any financial cost, and yes, it is easier to relax.

The more relaxed you can be, the greater advantage will be gained in the training period.

To demonstrate the way in which anyone can use stretches in their daily routines and jobs around the house and garden, as part of a wider programme of flexibility training for health and/or sport, here are some examples. These are not the only exercises possible and, indeed, the cyclist can pick his selection and the footballer his, to slot into these times. See p.71 for the key to the stretches. Each stretch is explained in full in Chapter 7.

7.00 a.m. Wake up: 10 mins in bed, E1, D1, D2, D3, C13.
7.10 a.m. Get up: 5 mins on floor, A1, B3, B6.
7.20 a.m. Shower: 10 mins stand/kneel, E3, C4, C12.
7.30 a.m. Drying: 5 mins sit/stand, C4 C1.

The washing and drying can be done in only a few moments but by elongating the process a little you gain the training effect. Washing the toes or knees while stretching the hamstrings or drying your hair while stretching the arms and neck areas is a good use of time for the busy person. Children need to be washed and dressed too and you can also use that time to stretch out – it might help control or reduce the early morning 'grumps' for some who suffer from them as you will just have to relax!

6.30 a.m. Woken up: 2 mins change nappy, C5.

6.35 a.m. Make tea: 5 mins in kitchen, A4, A5.

6.45 a.m. Drink tea: 10 mins back in bed, A6, A3, A7.

7.00 a.m. Dress kids: 10 mins stand/kneel, C1, B8, B7.

All these examples are trying to take advantage of being in the most relaxed and warmest state of the day. Dressing, shaving and putting on make-up might also offer good static opportunities when specific stretches could be performed in a similar way and while you are still nicely warm. Maybe later:

8.00 a.m. Reading paper: 10 mins floor sit, E2, C5, C2.

8.15 a.m. Washing up: 10 mins standing, B2.

The day will provide every opportunity to stretch if you are uninhibited and inventive, but how about warming up first? We have seen that the bed and the shower or bath can passively warm you and, of course, just being indoors will make things better than most sports venues.

Nevertheless, as you stretch more and hold the stretch longer it becomes more important to make sure you are as warm as possible. Naturally you should use all the passive ways to be warm – clothes, central heating and fires – but you can be active in warm-up as well – strip the bed, turn a mattress and make up the bed again – then spend 5 minutes stretching and resting. The stairs can be mounted a bit faster or a few times to get the body ready; outside in the garden, digging, mowing, sweeping and DIY all put up the metabolic rate and can be used gently to prepare the muscles for stretching.

This section refers to the 'home' but naturally the notion can be expanded to many other situations – the thing is to get into the habit. Walking the dog can warm you up, then while the dog runs you can stretch. Going to work you mix walking (warming times) and waiting at the bus stop or train station or sitting on the train (stretching times). Sitting in the office at your desk, waiting in the cafeteria queue and during those long meetings the time can be used.

Wherever you are, see what can be used or changed to get a good stretch. There are lots of ways of sitting and standing in order to stretch different muscles – just be inventive.

SUMMARY OF THE BASIC TECHNIQUES

GETTING READY TO STRETCH

1. *Dress in clothing which does not resist the movement.* Loose clothing, little clothing or no clothing, depending on the circumstances. At work, you may have to leave the thigh stretches till you get home; however, the calves could be stretched without risk to your clothes.

2. *Always feel warm and be warm.* This might mean trotting up stairs a couple of times before you start, or stretching in the bath or shower. Sauna rooms and jacuzzis are ideal for some stretching.

3. *Relaxation before you start.* Breathe slowly and deeply, try to feel your muscles getting heavy and soft. It sometimes helps if you tense them up a bit at first, then relax.

DOING THE STRETCHES

4. *Choose the stretch and check your alignment.* Once you are familiar with your programme of stretches this will become automatic. However, this initial set-up is crucial and you should regularly check in a mirror that you are actually doing what you think you are doing.

5. *Maintain the relaxation in the target muscle.* Breathe all the while – do not hold your breath. Stay aware of the muscle you are stretching, its softness and heaviness.

6a. *Stretch slowly and with minimum effort.* There should be no jerky movements, only a steady, single, controlled move to the point of resistance.

6b. *Hold this initial final (primary) position for at least 10 seconds.* The held position applies the stretch and with practice will become easier to hold.

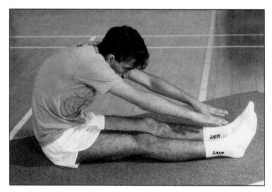

6c. *Move the stretch to a new final (full) position and hold – 10 to 30 seconds.* This extension applies the useful stretch but can only be achieved safely after the initial stretch.

6d. *Repeating the sequence.* If you feel good, have time and are interested in improving your flexibility more quickly, then, as long as you maintain good form and relaxation, repeat the whole sequence a few more times.

GENERAL POINTS

7. *Competition is never safe in stretching.* The requirement for relaxation and slowness makes competition really inappropriate. When working in groups the normal sporting, 'go for it', 'beat that if you can', mentality and practices will only reduce the effectiveness of the training.

8. *Keep stretching symmetrical.* Do not favour one side of the body, unless there is a clear discrepancy between, say, one thigh and the other. In such cases get medical confirmation before starting a programme.

9. *Recognize how you feel and act accordingly.* Do not expect always to stretch as far as last time, but accept the daily fluctuations in your responses to a stretch and do not overstretch.

10. *Regularly check your alignment.* Go back to the diagrams and figures to check up on your style.

11. *You do not have to do your complete programme at one time.* Fit it in as and when you can – just keep chipping away.

12. *Try to check your breathing and feel the muscles as the stretch progresses.* This is a conscious mental task of concentration and application to detail. It does not mean you cannot do other things but every now and again check your efforts are relaxed.

WARM-UP AND WARM-DOWN

Warm-up allows the body to prepare for exercise by the optimization of the physical and mechanical properties of tissue and thus it establishes metabolic, neuromuscular and circulatory efficiency. The result of this should be better performances and less sports injury, particularly to muscle.

Warm-down is a strategy aimed at reducing unwanted effects of exercise like the muscle soreness which builds up over the days after exhaustive exercise. Warm-down is not relevant to flexibility training as stretching is a relaxation in itself. However, stretching out after exercise is often used as the basis of a warm-down and this can be usefully extended into a training session on flexibility. The exercise period has become the warm-up for the flexibility training which will nicely double as the warm-down to the exercise.

There are three types of warm-up strategy, namely, passive general, active general and active specific.

Passive general warm-up: This is simply any non-active way of raising the body temperature, such as a hot shower, bath, jacuzzi or sauna. It could be utilizing the fact you have been in bed, or sitting in front of a fire or sunbathing on a very hot day, and are thus thoroughly warm. High skin temperature does not in itself mean your deep muscles are hot enough, so you may need to add to the passive warm-up with a little extra active warm-up. You should be able to recognize how warm (and relaxed) you are by how the muscles respond to stretching in comparison to last time.

The major advantages of passive warm-up are that it does not waste stored energy which could otherwise be available for the exercise to follow (although this does not matter in flexibility training) and they are by nature relaxing. The possible disadvantage of passive warm-up for training other attributes and in competition, is that it does not activate the muscles or practise the skills. Passive warm-up may, therefore, be best for flexibility work and endurance activities rather than the more explosive ones. As a final point, it might be advisable to use the passive and relaxed method to reduce the anxiety of the over-aroused performer, but avoid it for the under-aroused player who needs 'geeing up' prior to activity.

Active general warm-up: This uses light exercise of a simple and overall nature, such as jogging or cycling or moving rhythmically to music. It always starts at a very low rate of energy output, and increases slowly over time to say about 20 per cent of maximum. Warm clothes are used to retain the heat and as high an ambient temperature as possible is chosen. Normal room temperatures of 22–25° C are best and the activity may need to continue for quite a while to achieve optimum results. Environmental conditions (how cold, windy it is, etc.), your clothing, level of fitness (fitter people take longer to warm through because they are better at losing heat), the specific warm-up to be done and the activity to follow, will all have a bearing on the time spent on general warm-up.

As a rough guide for flexibility work which is not going to follow directly some other activity period, and is going to be in a reasonably warm environment, 10 to 20 minutes of general active warm-up seems about right. Followed by a little specific warm-up on each muscle to be stretched. The bigger the muscle group to be worked on, the more warm-up required.

Active specific warm-up: This uses the specific muscles about to be targetted in the activity to follow. For soccer, this would involve increasingly intense sprints and jinking runs, kicking, jumping and so on. Each sport needs to mimic the major activities about to be undertaken. Specific warm-up follows general warm-up.

For flexibility, one chooses the activity which fits the situation. If you are generally nicely warmed up and are about to start stretching the shoulder region, then a few minutes actively swinging and rotating the arms and shoulders should precede the stretches. Again the bigger the muscle groups, the more warm-up required.

Flexibility is slow and not active so as the training continues you tend to cool down, thus further warm-up may well be necessary at times as the session progresses.

A final practical comment is worth making, and that is, if you are doing proper SASS then even if you are not fully warmed up you will not do damage. You may find that you seem less flexible but as long as you stick to the rules no damage is possible. From the realistic point of view, for flexibility training the more you can use those occasions when you have already been warmed up by passive means or by an activity you have just completed, then the more time will be saved.

GUIDELINES FOR PLANNING WARM-UP

1. Gradually increase intensity and range.
2. Use rhythmical and unresisted movements up to full active ranges.
3. Let one exercise flow naturally into the next without jerky changes.
4. Do not leave out any parts of the body,

but spend more time on the bigger muscles.

5. Use relaxation techniques during the warm-up.

6. Avoid all isometrics, breath holding, resisted movements or maximum efforts.

REFERENCES

Alter, M. J., *Science of Stretching*, Human Kinetics, 1988

Anderson, B., *Stretching*, Pelham Books, 1980

Beaulieu J. E., *Stretching for all Sports,* The Athletic Press (California), 1980

Beaulieu J. E., 'Developing a Stretching Program', *Physician and Sports Medicine* 9 (11): pp. 59–69, 1981

Borms, J., Van Roy, P., Santens, J–P. and Haentjens A., 'Optimal Duration of Static Stretching Exercises for Improvement of Coxo-femoral Flexibility', *Journal of Sports Sciences* 5: pp39–47, 1987

de Vries, H. A., 'Evaluation of Static Stretching Procedures for Improvement of Flexibility, *Research Quarterly* 33: pp222–8, May 1962

McNaught-Davis, J. P., *Developing Flexibility* (Resource Pack), National Coaching Foundation, 1986

McNaught-Davis, J. P., *Developing Flexibility* (Video), Brighton Polytechnic, Media Services, Watts Bld., Brighton.

Wiktorsson-Moller, M., Oberg B., Eskstrand, J. and Gillquist, J., 'Effects of Warming up, Massage and Stretching on Range of Motion and Muscle Strength in the Lower Extremity', *American Journal of Sports Medicine* 11(4): pp249–52, 1983

Williford, H. N., East J. B., Smith F. H. and Burry, L. A., 'Evaluation of Warm-up for Improvement in Flexibility', *American Journal of Sports-medicine* 14(4): pp316–9, 1986

7

STRETCHING EXERCISES (SASS)

This chapter contains a series of stretching exercises which have been grouped in various ways to fulfil different sport-related needs.

First, there is the section which illustrates a set of stretches suitable for fundamental flexibility training for every sport. This gives the building blocks for a good basic training programme which would develop ranges of motion, safely and steadily, in a balanced and relatively unbiased way. Every programme of flexibility training should involve at least one of the alternative stretches from each muscle group section. Over a period of time, and along the lines of the Sample Repeating Two-day Programme in Chapter 6, your basic pattern of exercises can be developed. By increasing the number of repetitions of the full set in a given period, according to time available and requirements (based on individual need and present flexibility), this would form your training programme.

Second, there are some sets of stretches

which can be selected as *additions* or *extensions* to the basic programme. These are suggested as extra stretches to enhance the specific flexibilities which, being emphasized through the types of skills and movements associated with specific sports, may also need to be emphasized in training. They provide, as well, some alternatives which can be exchanged for those basic exercises which no longer take you far enough because your flexibility has outgrown them. The selection of these stretches will be very individual and should reflect a realistic appraisal of your own flexibility strengths and weaknesses in relation to your sport. A coach or mentor can be the best assistant in the assessment of such needs.

Both the basic and the extension programmes use only the SASS technique.

GENERAL RULES FOR ALL STRETCHES

1. Nothing you do should be painful or uncomfortable. If it is, stop at once and check your method again. If it is still as bad, do not do that stretch but choose an alternative. Do not persist with any painful stretches. Everyone is different and not all the stretches suggested will be right for you.

2. Relaxation as you do the stretches is very important; so keep breathing and concentrate on letting tension flow away throughout the stretch. Relaxation can be practised independently of your stretching training and for the serious sports performer it really should be.

3. Never do stretching training unless you are really warm. Passive or active warming is an essential part of this training. Stretching is a slow process and you may need to re-warm during the training session. Jogging, cycling or any big total body activity are good for warming up. Remember the bigger the muscle group being stretched the more warm-up you may need. An ideal time to stretch is after a period of hard play or other training when you are really hot. When you do the stretches it is often better to keep the body clothed to keep heat in. Always make sure the clothes are loose though, because the idea is to stretch the muscles, not the clothing!

4. Any stretch which is asymmetrical must be repeated for the other side of the body; i.e. left leg hamstrings followed by right leg hamstrings. In the text below, the stretches which are symmetrical have been designated *single* requiring only the one stretch for balanced training, and the asymmetrical ones as *double* needing a repeat on the other side to achieve the same balance. This instruction is independent of how many stretch repeats you undertake in a period of training. On some occasions a *PLUS* has been added to the single or double classification. This signifies that a stretch is really more than one stretch although it retains its basic symmetry or asymmetry.

5. Especially for the stiff individual and/or the beginner, think of these exercises as 'your eventual aim' and do not think they all need doing in their entirety to get any benefit. In fact it would be much better to do the stretches as far as the initial stretch and ignore the final stretch if this will keep you doing them. A number of coaches have reported that the stiffer an athlete is, the less he or she stretches. Also, even the flexible ones tend to ignore

their worst areas for those muscles which are already good.

STRETCHING EXERCISES FOR SPORT – THE BASIC PROGRAMME

The stretches are arranged with reference letters and numbers to allow an easy short-hand for making up programmes and commentary in the text. In this section there are five groups of basic stretches:

A group (7 stretches) includes the upper body stretches, covering the upper arms, shoulders and neck and are collectively known as the UPPERS.

B group (8 stretches) includes the trunk, pelvis and back stretches and has the title of MIDS.

C group (13 stretches) has the LOWERS and concentrates on the leg, top and bottom.

D group (4 stretches) is a small section on the extremities of fingers, hands, feet and toes. Called here the EXTREMITIES.

E group (3 stretches) are just a few all-over stretches; known as the TOTALS.

These classifications may give the impression that all the stretches are very specific and there is no overlap – this is quite wrong. A number of the stretches stretch muscles in other groups, but on the whole their main job is in their designated group.

A GROUP: THE UPPERS
Title: **CAT STRETCH**
Body Area: ARMS, SHOULDERS, SIDES OF TRUNK
Reference Number: A1
Type: single

Method: Kneel with the soles of the feet pointing upwards. Keeping the head in the line of the spine and facing the floor, creep the hands forward at shoulder width apart. Keep the bottom down and stretch forwards.

HOLD AT THE POINT OF RESISTANCE FOR 10 SECONDS

Creep forward again slowly to new point of resistance.

HOLD AT THE NEW POINT OF RESISTANCE FOR 10–30 SECONDS

Slowly return to the starting position.

Points to note:
1. You may find that your chest feels cramped a little so pay attention to steady breathing – do not hold your breath.
2. Your knees may become painful on a hard surface and this will stop you feeling relaxed, so use a folded blanket or cushion if it is uncomfortable without.
3. Your knees can be placed slightly apart if this is more comfortable.
4. If you pull your bottom down a little as you reach the point of final resistance it will increase the stretch a little more.

Title: **FLAT-CAT STRETCH**
Body Area: TOPS ARMS, SHOULDERS, TRUNK SIDES
Reference Number: A2
Type: single

Method: Lying face down on a comfortable but firm surface, stretch your arms out in front and gently interlace the fingers. Then lift your arms off the floor until resistance is felt in the back of the shoulders and upper arms.

HOLD AT THE POINT OF RESISTANCE FOR 10 SECONDS

Then see if you can raise the arms to a new stretch position a little higher.

HOLD AT THE POINT OF NEW RESISTANCE FOR 10–20 SECONDS

Points to note:
1. This is not an easy stretch and might be one you work at a little as your general fitness improves.
2. The stretch is passive but you have to do some work to make it happen. Some support for the arms can be arranged with a firm cushion under the hands to give a little rest.
3. It is easy to hold your breath during this exercise and this must be avoided.

4. This is a good exercise because it supports the spine and keeps it straight on the floor.
5. For those with stiff shoulders you will get a stretch without lifting the arms.

Title: **TALL-CAT STRETCH**
Body Area: INNER SIDE ARMS, SHOULDERS AND TRUNK
Reference Number: A3
Type: single

Method: Extend the arms above the head with the hands placed so the palm of one is against the back of the other. Stretch straight upwards and slightly backwards with the arms.

HOLD AT THE POINT OF RESISTANCE FOR 10 SECONDS

Then stretch again to new position.

HOLD AT THE NEW POINT OF RESISTANCE FOR 10–30 SECONDS

Points to note:
1. The back is unsupported so be extra careful to keep it straight.
2. Placing the feet slightly apart will add stability to the exercise.
3. Again keep breathing steadily.

Stretches A1, A2, A3 are all good alternatives and can be interchanged for each other according to the conditions under which you are stretching.

Title: **SHOULDER PULL-DOWN**
Body Area: SIDE OF NECK AND TOP AND SIDE SHOULDER, ARM
Reference Number: A4
Type: double

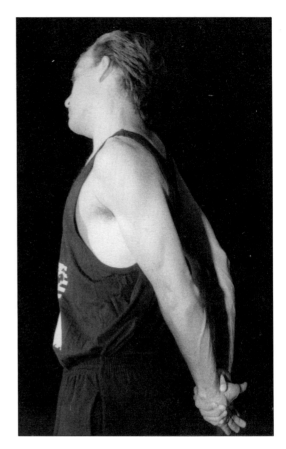

Method: Leaning the head to one side, say the left shoulder, start to pull the right arm down and across the back until resistance is felt in the top of the shoulder and neck.

HOLD AT THE POINT OF RESISTANCE FOR 10 SECONDS

A further pull will achieve a further stretch once the initial stretch has happened.

HOLD AT THE NEW POINT OF RESISTANCE FOR 10–30 SECONDS

Points to note:
1. Keeping your back straight and tilting your head is the main thing to check.

2. One arm is being active, the other must be passive and this is too easy at first, so practise and be gentle with yourself.

Title: **SHOULDER PULL-ACROSS**
Body Area: MID UPPER BACK, SHOULDER, UPPER ARM
Reference Number: A5
Type: double

Method: Bring the elbow of one arm across the chest at the level of the shoulder using the hand of the free arm. The stretch is felt in the middle of the upper back across the shoulder of the arm being moved and down that arm towards the elbow.

**HOLD AT THE POINT OF RESISTANCE
FOR 10 SECONDS**

After the initial stretch a further movement can be achieved.

**HOLD AT THE NEW POINT OF RESISTANCE
FOR 10–30 SECONDS**

Points to note:
1. Standing with your back against a wall will help to keep the trunk from twisting as the arm is pulled.
2. The arm is acting like a lever and a small force applied at the elbow can be magnified to dangerous levels at the back; so take it easy with the pull.

3. As with A4 active relaxation in the arm to be pulled is necessary to achieve a good stretch.

Title: **SHOULDER PULL-UP**
Body Area: BACK UPPER ARM, TOP SHOULDER, SIDE TRUNK
Reference Number: A6
Type: double

Method: Holding the bent elbow of the arm to be stretched with the free hand, with the arm vertically above your head, pull the elbow behind your head until the resistance is felt in the back upper arm and the shoulder. Also stretch down the side.

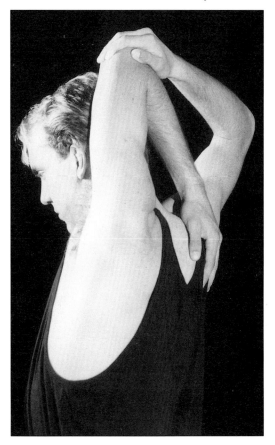

HOLD AT THE POINT OF RESISTANCE FOR 10 SECONDS

Give a second pull to the new final position.

HOLD AT THE NEW POINT OF RESISTANCE FOR 10–30 SECONDS

Points to note:
1. Do not lean out of the vertical while doing this exercise. Try sitting in an upright chair for support, or stand against a wall.
2. The same points about positive relaxation of the arm being stretched apply here, too – try waggling the fingers occasionally to help the process.
3. This is another lever so take care.

Stretches A4, A5, A6 are all similar but not really alternatives as they pull in fairly different directions. They could be interchanged for each other according to the conditions under which you are stretching and the time you have but try to avoid favouring one over either of the others.

Title: **NECK PULL**
Body Area: ALL ROUND NECK, FRONT, BACK, SIDES
Reference Number: A7
Type: double PLUS

Method: Lean head to one side and hold at point of resistance.

HOLD AT THE POINT OF RESISTANCE FOR 10 SECONDS

Move a little more in same direction.

HOLD AT THE NEW POINT OF RESISTANCE FOR 10–30 SECONDS

Relax, and move head to new position and repeat as above. Do this all the way round in, say, eight distinct stretches, until back at starting place.

Points to note:
1. Continuous rotations of the neck to stretch the muscles are considered by some as dangerous, so this method avoids this. Personally, I am not convinced that it is really dangerous, as long as it is slow and controlled; however, the method above is certainly safe.
2. Keep the shoulders down.
3. Keep the body vertical, sitting or standing.

B GROUP: THE MIDS
Title: **FLAT-CHEST**
Body Area: CHEST, SHOULDERS AND UPPER ARMS
Reference Number: B1
Type: single

Method: Lying face down, interlace your fingers behind your back (if you can), then lift the extended arms straight up

until the stretch is felt across the chest and in the shoulders and arms.

HOLD AT THE POINT OF RESISTANCE FOR 10 SECONDS

Push a little further and then

HOLD AT THE NEW POINT OF RESISTANCE FOR 10–20 SECONDS

Points to note:
1. Rather like A2 this has a strength component which may need to be worked on.
2. Note all the points as in A2.

Title: **TOWEL CHEST**
Body Area: CHEST AND SHOULDER
Reference Number: B2
Type: single PLUS

Method: Hold a towel or bar in both hands with enough distance between the hands to allow the hands, with arms straight, to be taken over the head. Stop at

**HOLD AT EACH POINT OF RESISTANCE FOR
10–30 SECONDS**

Points to note:
1. This is really many stretches and each time you do the exercise you should pick just a few points and vary these over a period of weeks.
2. Keep the back straight and the head looking straight forward.

Title: **BACK ROLL**
Body Area: ALL BACK AND ROUND HIPS
Reference Number: B3
Type: single

various points of resistance during the travel.

**HOLD AT EACH POINT OF RESISTANCE
FOR 10 SECONDS**

and then

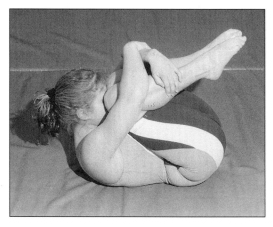

Method: Sit on a solid but comfortable surface and pull the knees into the chest with the arms across them. Tuck the head down towards the chest. Gently roll up and down on the spine about six times, increasing the pull a little as you go.

Point to note:
1. Keep your toes pointed.

Title: **LEG OVER**
Body Area: LOWER BACK, SIDE HIP
Reference Number: B4
Type: double

Method: Lying on your back on the floor with one arm straight out from the shoulder at right angles to the body, use the other arm to direct the opposite leg, bent at 90 degrees, up and over the other leg. Turn your head to look at the outstretched arm. Pull the leg down until resistance is felt in the lower back and over the buttocks.

HOLD AT THE POINT OF RESISTANCE
FOR 10 SECONDS

With another pull down the final stretch can be achieved.

HOLD AT THE NEW POINT OF RESISTANCE
FOR 10–30 SECONDS

Point to note:
1. Keep the back flat on the floor.

Title: **TUCK**
Body Area: BACK, BACKS OF LEGS
Reference Number: B5
Type: single

Method: Lie down with the back of the head in contact with the floor and the lower back flat. Pull both knees up towards the chest with the hands until some resistance is felt in the back and the backs of the legs.

HOLD AT THE POINT OF RESISTANCE
FOR 10 SECONDS

Pull to the final position and

HOLD AT THE NEW POINT OF RESISTANCE
FOR 10–30 SECONDS

Point to note:
1. Remember not to stop breathing during the stretch.

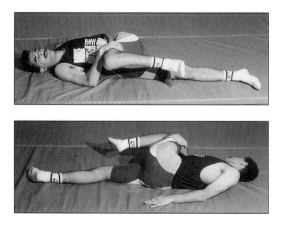

Title: **TWISTER**
Body Area: TOP THIGH, BUTTOCKS, SIDE BACK
Reference Number: B6
Type: double

Method: Sit on the floor with back straight, bend one leg and cross it over the straight one. Bend the arm (on same side as straight leg) and place it along the outside of the bent leg just above the knee. Keeping the bent leg still with this arm, turn the head to look over the shoulder of the straight arm, which supports the body. Thus the upper body is twisted until resistance is felt along the bent thigh, buttocks and back.

HOLD AT THE POINT OF RESISTANCE
FOR 10 SECONDS

Twist a little further, maintaining the right position.

HOLD AT THE NEW POINT OF RESISTANCE
FOR 10–30 SECONDS

Points to note:
1. This is not easy to get correct and there will be a lot of variety from person to person where the stretch is felt.
2. Take care not to pull the back fast but go slowly and gently.

Title: **VOLUNTEER**
Body Area: SIDE TRUNK, CHEST AND SHOULDER
Reference Number: B7
Type: double

Method: Lying with knees bent and feet flat on the floor one arm is stretched down towards the feet while the other is stretched up above the head. Both arms are kept flat to the floor. Stretch till resistance is felt along the side with arm above head.

HOLD AT THE POINT OF RESISTANCE
FOR 10 SECONDS

Move the arm up to new resistance point.

HOLD AT THE NEW POINT OF RESISTANCE
FOR 10–30 SECONDS

Point to note:
1. If you are stiff in the shoulders then the raised arm may be slightly off the floor but keep it straight.

Title: **STRADDLE LEAN**
Body Area: HAMSTRINGS, ANKLES, INSIDE OF UPPER LEG, LOWER BACK AND INSIDE OF SHOULDERS
Reference Number: B8 (also used as a Total E2)
Type: double

Method: Start this exercise sitting in the straddle position, with legs straight and back upright. Point the toes and rotate the shoulders slowly lowering one shoulder towards the inside of the lower leg.

**HOLD AT THE POINT OF RESISTANCE
FOR 10 SECONDS**

Rotate and lower a little more to the final position and

**HOLD AT THE NEW POINT OF RESISTANCE
FOR 10–30 SECONDS**

Points to note:
1. Avoid bending forward.
2. This is an easy exercise to bounce if you are not careful.

All these B group stretches or MIDS tend to overlap a little but ring the changes to get a balanced programme.

C GROUP: LOWERS
Title: **HAMS**
Body Area: HAMSTRINGS
Reference Number: C1
Type: double

Method: Sit on the floor and rest the sole of one foot against the extended right thigh of the other leg. Keep the foot of the extended leg dorsally flexed (toes pulled towards knee). Hold onto the extended leg with both hands at about the level of the knee, and bend forward sliding the hands down the leg until resistance is felt

in the thigh. The bend is from the hips so the back is straight. A towel held in both hands and placed around the extended foot can also be used.

HOLD AT THE POINT OF RESISTANCE FOR 10 SECONDS

Push a little further until the new resistance point.

HOLD AT THE NEW POINT OF RESISTANCE FOR 10–30 SECONDS

Points to note:
1. It is easy to use the back but this must be avoided.
2. Focus your eyes on a point on the floor about five feet ahead.

Title: **KNEE CHEST**
Body Area: HAMSTRINGS
Reference Number: C2
Type: double

Method: The method is the same as B8 above except that only one leg is pulled up at a time.
Point to note:
1. *See* B8.

Title: **BOTTOMS UP**
Body Area: HAMSTRINGS AND LOWER SPINE
Reference Number: C3
Type: single

Method: Although this can be done sitting or standing the name comes from the standing position. Standing with knees bent and feet shoulder-width apart, put both hands on the floor palms down. Slowly straighten the legs until resistance is felt in the hamstrings and/or back. The sitting version is really a two-legged type of C1 above, but the knees are never fully straightened.

HOLD AT THE POINT OF RESISTANCE FOR 10 SECONDS

Go to new maximum and hold again.

HOLD AT THE NEW POINT OF RESISTANCE FOR 10–30 SECONDS

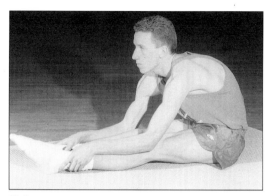

Points to note:
1. For the already very flexible, the standing variant can be conducted on steps with the feet one step higher than the hands.
2. For the stiffer individuals cushions can be placed under the hands in the bottoms up case.
3. The sitting exercise probably will not produce a stretch for the more flexible individuals.

Title: **BUDDHA**
Body Area: GROIN
Reference Number: C4
Type: single

Method: Sit with soles of feet held together by your hands and back straight. The elbows which will be resting on your knees press the legs down towards the floor until resistance is felt in the groin.

HOLD AT THE POINT OF RESISTANCE FOR 10 SECONDS

An additional press will attain the final position.

HOLD AT THE NEW POINT OF RESISTANCE FOR 10–30 SECONDS

Points to note:
1. Any bending must come from the hips only with back straight.
2. Keep the eyes focused on a point about five feet ahead on the floor.

Title: **GROIN STRADDLE**
Body Area: GROIN
Reference Number: C5
Type: single

Method: Sitting on the floor with legs comfortably apart and extended, the hands are placed at about the level of the knees. Bend forward from the hips until the groin is taut and there is resistance.

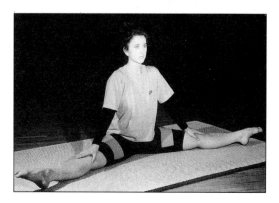

**HOLD AT THE POINT OF RESISTANCE
FOR 10 SECONDS**

Then tilt forward a little more to attain the new position.

**HOLD AT THE NEW POINT OF RESISTANCE
FOR 10–30 SECONDS**

Points to note:
1. The back must be kept straight.
2. Keep the eyes focused on a point about five feet ahead on the floor.

Title: **GROIN LUNGE**
Body Area: GROIN
Reference Number: C6
Type: double

Method: Standing with feet pointing ahead take one foot out to the side into a wide stance. Bend one leg and shift the weight over that foot so the straight leg feels a stretch in the groin.

**HOLD AT THE POINT OF RESISTANCE
FOR 10 SECONDS**

With care push a little further to a new resistance point.

**HOLD AT THE NEW POINT OF RESISTANCE
FOR 10–30 SECONDS**

Point to note:
1. This is an exercise where there is a temptation to bounce which must be resisted. The sideways thrust must be under control throughout.

Title: **LYING GROIN**
Body Area: GROIN
Reference Number: C7
Type: single

Method: This starts from the position taken up in C4: Buddha but you lie back and allow the weight of your legs to create the pull. Relax into the stretch for about 30–60 seconds at a time.

Point to note:
1. This is quite a good relaxation pose to adopt while listening to music or in bed as you are waking up.

Title: **CHAISE-LONGUE**
Body Area: QUADRICEPS AND ANKLE
Reference Number: C8
Type: double

Method: Lying on your side with your head supported in your hand, grasp the free leg with the free hand at the foot. You can then pull the ankle gently back towards the upper hip.

HOLD AT THE POINT OF RESISTANCE FOR 10 SECONDS

A further pull achieves the final position.

HOLD AT THE NEW POINT OF RESISTANCE FOR 10–30 SECONDS

Point to note:
1. Pull leg towards hip, do not bend back towards the foot.

Title: **QUEUEING**
Body Area: QUADRICEPS AND ANKLE
Reference Number: C9
Type: double

Method: This is a standing variant of C8 above and can be done on those occasions when you can't lie down. You do need a

solid support like a wall and the back needs to be kept from twisting. Supporting yourself against the wall with one hand, use your free hand to grasp the opposite leg. Gently pull the ankle back towards the upper hip. Exactly the same preliminary and final stretch can be achieved as in C8.

Point to note:
1. *See* C8.

Title: **QUADRICEPS LUNGE**
Body Area: QUADRICEPS
Reference Number: C10
Type: double

Method: From the standing position, put one leg forward and bend it, bearing your weight on the hands as well as the feet with the forward knee directly over the ankle. You can now let your hips drop down under control. Neither knee should move during this procedure. The stretch will be felt all down the front thigh.

HOLD AT THE POINT OF RESISTANCE
FOR 10 SECONDS

Drop the hips a little more, maintaining the knee positions.

HOLD AT THE NEW POINT OF RESISTANCE
FOR 10–30 SECONDS

Point to note:
1. The area of stretch can be changed by slowly turning the hip to the inside.

Title: **ACHILLES' HEEL**
Body Area: BACK OF LOWER LEG, SOLEUS AND ACHILLES
Reference Number: C11
Type: double

Method: Lean against a support like a wall, facing this support squarely. Keep the arms and back straight. Put one foot a small pace forward with knee bent. Press the hips down and press the knee under the hips in or forward. Keep both heels on the ground. The pull will be felt low in the leg furthest from the wall.

HOLD AT THE POINT OF RESISTANCE
FOR 10 SECONDS

Press down and forward a little more and

HOLD AT THE NEW POINT OF RESISTANCE
FOR 10–30 SECONDS

Points to note:
1. Avoid any twisting at the knee or back – keep square.
2. Make sure the feet are pointing forward (heels on the ground) and not to the side, i.e. in the same plane as the legs.
3. You are using body weight so take it steady and do not allow yourself to bounce the stretch.

Title: **CALF STRETCH**
Body Area: BACK OF THE CALF FROM KNEE TO ANKLE
Reference Number: C12
Type: double

Method: This is very similar to C11 above, but there are subtle differences. The support of a wall is again required and you must be square to it. You may need to be a bit closer and more upright this time. It is again the back leg that is stretched, but it is straight and only the forward leg is bent a little. The movement of the hips is more forward than down – the heels again firmly grounded.

**HOLD AT THE POINT OF RESISTANCE
FOR 10 SECONDS**

Again press to the new position and

**HOLD AT THE NEW POINT OF RESISTANCE
FOR 10–30 SECONDS**

Point to note:
1. *See* C11.

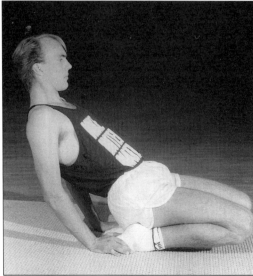

Title: **SHIN STRETCH**
Body Area: FRONT OF LOWER LEG (AND FEET)
Reference Number: C13
Type: single

Method: Take up a kneeling position with the top of the feet flat to the floor – sitting on heels with back straight. This may be enough stretch in itself. Or for greater stretch, if you can without pain, move the trunk backwards.

**HOLD AT THE POINT OF RESISTANCE
FOR 10 SECONDS**

Points to note:
1. If you have weak or painful knees you may find this an inappropriate stretch.
2. You can sit, instead, and do one leg at a time by placing your hand on the knee and the other at the foot and then gently pulling them apart.

D GROUP: THE EXTREMITIES

In this set of exercises you are going to work on all the multiplicity of movements in hands, fingers, wrists and the feet, toes and ankles. The basic starting point is to get comfortable and work on one hand with the other or one foot with both hands and then repeat for the other. This can take a long while if you wish and is ideal for the bath, bed or sitting watching the television.

In each area you should methodically work through all the natural movements pushing or pulling the tissue gently to the various points of resistance. Try and compare the stiffness in one foot or hand with the other. An old injury may mean that selected areas of stiffness have grown up and caused an imbalance from one to the other.

The basic principles apply. Hold at the points of resistance for a few seconds and then apply a little more stretch.

Title: **ANKLE ROTATION**
Body Area: ANKLE AND FOOT
Reference Number: D1
Type: double

Method: Take one ankle in one hand and pull the foot with the other hand placed near the toes. Sequentially, pull to stretched position and then rotate ankle a little to new

position and repeat. Eventually returning to original position having done a whole circle.

Title: **TOES STRETCH**
Body Area: TOES
Reference Number: D2
Type: double

Method: First, take all the toes together in your hand and stretch them first forward and hold, then back and hold. Then take each toe in turn holding the various stretched positions.

Title: **WRIST ROTATION**
Body Area: WRIST AND HAND
Reference Number: D3
Type: double

Method: Repeat the D1 activity with the wrist instead of the ankle.

Title: **FINGERS STRETCH**
Body Area: FINGERS AND HAND
Reference Number: D4
Type: double

Method: This is an upper body repeat of the toes exercise in D2 above. There are more possibilities and you should do them all.

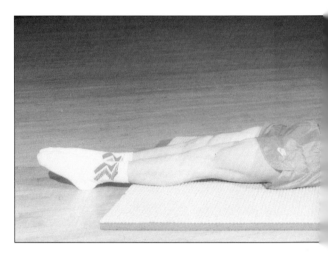

E GROUP: THE TOTALS

Title: **ELONGATION**
Body Area: TOTAL BODY STRETCH
Reference Number: E1
Type: single

Method: Lying flat on the floor, extend the legs and arms. Point the toes and stretch the fingers out fully until resistance is felt.

HOLD AT THE POINT OF RESISTANCE FOR 10 SECONDS

Again stretch to a new position and

HOLD AT THE NEW POINT OF RESISTANCE FOR 10–30 SECONDS

Points to note:
1. Do not let the back arch up.
2. Do not hold your breath.

Title: **STRADDLE LEAN**
Body Area: HAMSTRINGS, ANKLES, INSIDE OF UPPER LEG, LOWER BACK AND INSIDE OF SHOULDERS
Reference Number: E2 (also used as a MIDS B8)
Type: double

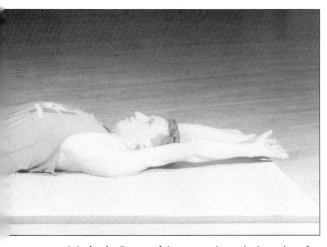

Method: Start this exercise sitting in the straddle position, with legs straight and back upright. Point the toes and rotate the shoulders slowly lowering one shoulder towards the inside of the lower leg.

HOLD AT THE POINT OF RESISTANCE FOR 10 SECONDS

Rotate and lower a little more to the final position and

HOLD AT THE NEW POINT OF RESISTANCE FOR 10–30 SECONDS

Points to note:
1. Avoid bending forward.
2. This is an easy exercise to bounce if you are not careful.

Title: **STANDING SIDE STRETCH**
Body Area: ALL THE WAY UP SIDE FROM KNEE TO ELBOW
Reference Number: E3
Type: single

Method: Place one hand on the hip and lift the other hand up and over the head bending it at the elbow. Keep legs straight and lean towards the hip with your hand on it.

HOLD AT THE POINT OF RESISTANCE FOR 10 SECONDS

Again press slowly to the final position and

HOLD AT THE NEW POINT OF RESISTANCE FOR 10–30 SECONDS

Points to note:
1. Avoid bending forward.
2. This is an easy exercise to bounce if you are not careful.

STRETCHING EXERCISES FOR SPORTS SKILLS – EXTENSION PROGRAMME

This section presents stretches which could be used as extensions to your basic programme. These extension exercises can be used to emphasize the muscular demands of particular types of sports.

In some texts a big thing is made about specific stretching programmes for specific sports, but there are no really clear-cut or even a major set of differences between many sports in this respect. Indeed, if you take time to look at what exercises are recommended by the experts for various sports, you will find that sport-specific programmes are very similar between sports. Swimmers may emphasize shoulders and back, and soccer players may need to bias their training towards leg mobility, but there is a huge overlap as both sports have skills of total body movement. The idea of some special, in the sense of unique, sport-specific set of exercises is misleading. Indeed, the following two notions would be more accurate:

1. Sports may require an emphasis through their movement and skill requirements which should be reflected in the flexibility programme.

2. Some specific sports require extraordinary degrees of flexibility and therefore these players may need advance stretches (Chapter 8).

An advantage of the 'easy-to-follow set of sport programme' is, of course, that no one has to think, but can just follow the blueprint. In some situations that may be useful, but really it cuts across the essential idea for *your programme* being designed for *you*. It totally ignores the individual differences from player to player.

So what follows are some more stretching exercises giving alternatives and/or additions to a basic programme you have organized for yourself from the stretches already given. The sports performer can slant his/her training appropriately by adding or replacing stretches. That is to say, if you are a racket player with restricted overhead range you could extend the basic programme with some of the appropriate upper body extension stretches. Another player from the same sport might be restricted by their lack of upper leg range and would need to emphasize hamstring, groin and quadriceps work.

Another use for these extension exercises, and even the advanced stretches, is to replace exercises which no longer stretch the target area fully. Training will improve your flexibility and the exercises you initially use may eventually fail to stretch you as efficiently. The following exercises contain a number of very demanding ones which may be useful as your flexibility improves but would at present not be appropriate.

In order to pick appropriate extra or alternative stretches you must have a good notion of your weaknesses. There are two useful approaches to this problem, both of which need to be undertaken: first, use an outside (expert) agency. This can take the form of a coach or trustworthy sports friend whom you ask to observe your movements in terms of their 'fullness' of active range. This can be best assisted by video if this is available; second, in the passive situation put yourself in every extreme position that is likely to occur in your sport and assess, with help if possible, where you fall short of the optimum. So, for the squash player, what is your biggest passive lunge into the front, side and back walls? Is the main restriction in legs, back, shoulders? By asking and answering these questions you will identify the extension exercises you personally need.

As with the previous stretches there is a reference number for ease of recording on programme sheets – the extension exercises all have 'X' and a number. Each exercise should be held for 10 seconds at the point of resistance and for 10–30 seconds at the new point of resistance, as for the previous stretches.

TO ENHANCE BASIC STRETCHES UPPERS A1–A6

Title: **BACK SCRATCH**
Body Area: SHOULDERS AND ARMS
Reference Number: X1
Type: double

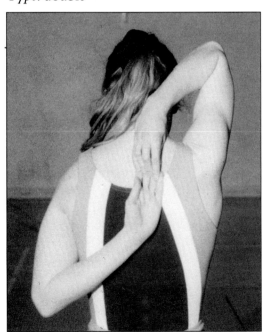

Method: From either a standing or sitting position use a towel or belt to link your hands behind your back. Make the distance between your two hands as small as possible. One elbow will be high, the other low. Hold the stretch. Pull your hands a little closer and hold at resistance for up to 30 seconds as usual.

Points to note:
1. Eventually you may be able to dispense with the towel and intertwine your fingers instead.
2. Do not twist away from the upright.

Title: **REVERSE PRAYER**
Body Area: SHOULDERS, ARMS, CHEST
Reference Number: X2
Type: single

Method: Again sitting or standing, put your arms behind your back so that the

palms meet and the fingers are pointing downwards. Try to rotate your hands together so that the fingers are pointing up. As your flexibility increases you will be able to take your hands further up your back.

Point to note:
1. As with many of these exercises you may not at first achieve the final position but persevere at the point of resistance and slowly, over the weeks, you will get closer to the ideal.

Title: **LIE BACK**
Body Area: SHOULDERS AND ARMS
Reference Number: X3
Type: single

Method: Start from sitting on the floor with your arms behind you, hands on the floor for support. Slide your arms further away as you lie back. Keep the legs straight out. Hold at limit for 10–30 seconds. The hands should stay close to each other as you go back. Again, this will be, for many, an exercise to which they will only fully aspire after some weeks or months of practice.

Title: **FOREARM TWIST**
Body Area: LOWER ARMS, BACK OF SHOULDERS
Reference Number: X4
Type: single

Method: Grasp a broom handle or some such object, with both hands in full internal rotation, then, still keeping the grip, bend the elbows towards a right angle. Hold the stretch, then try to further flex the elbows.

Points to note:
1. Keep your back as straight as possible.
2. Implement sports will benefit from the increased range of grip function.

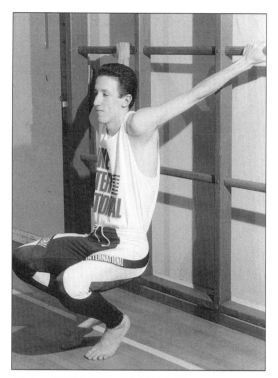

Title: **SHOULDER HANG**
Body Area: FRONT AND SIDE OF SHOULDERS
Reference Number: X5
Type: single

Method: Grasp a firm support like a wall bar behind your back with both hands using an overgrip. Hands should be about shoulder-width apart and the arms extended. Lowering the body by bending the knees will increase the stretch. Hold at resistance.

TO ENHANCE BASIC STRETCH UPPER A7
Title: **HEAD HANG 1**
Body Area: FRONT OF NECK
Reference Number: X6
Type: single

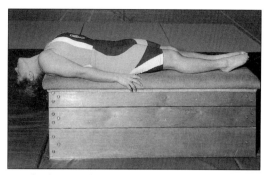

Method: Lie flat on your back on a firm surface, such as a table, allowing your head to hang over the edge.

Title: **HEAD HANG 2**
Body Area: BACK OF NECK
Reference Number: X7
Type: single

Method: Lie flat on your front on a firm surface allowing your head to hang over the edge. (Reverse position to photo for X6.)

Point to note:
1. To start with you may find it difficult to relax during these stretches, so make a conscious effort to breathe slowly and relax fully.

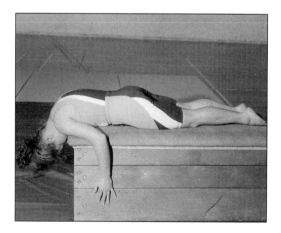

Title: **NECK PULL EXTENDED**
Body Area: ALL ROUND THE NECK, FRONT, BACK AND SIDES
Reference Number: X8
Type: double PLUS

Method: As with A7 lean the head to one side and hold at point of resistance. At this point use your hand to pull the stretch further. The shoulders must stay down and the trunk still. Do this standing or sitting.

Relax, and move the head to new position and repeat as above. Do this all the way round in, say, eight distinct stretches, until back at starting place.

Title: **HEAD ROLL**
Body Area: BACK OF NECK
Reference Number: X9
Type: single

Method: Kneel on both knees, lean forward and take your weight on the forearms with hands flat and palms down. Lean further forward until the crown of the head meets the floor. Slowly roll the head on the floor pushing the chin towards the chest. Hold at point of resistance.

Point to note:
1. These specific stretches are important for rugby forwards, wrestlers and other sports players likely to experience severe stretching of this sort in their game.

TO ENHANCE BASIC STRETCHES MIDS B1–B8

Title: **ARMCHAIR**
Body Area: SHOULDERS, CHEST AND PARTS OF BACK
Reference Number: X10 (kneeling) & X10a (standing)
Type: single

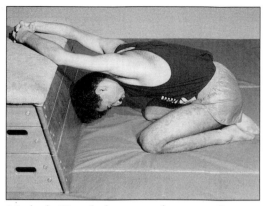

Method: Kneel far enough away from a chair to be able to lean forward onto it with arms folded above the head. The forearms and knees support should allow the head to drop down. Breathe out letting the chest and head weight pull down. The stretch can be enhanced after about 6–10 seconds with another relaxing exhalation.

Points to note:
1. You need a comfortable surface to kneel on.
2. Do not actively force down, just concentrate on relaxing and gravity and body weight will do the rest.
3. This can also be done standing, by leaning with arms straight and holding onto a barre, and lowering the head as before.

Title: **BACK ACHE**
Body Area: CHEST, SHOULDERS, FRONT THIGH
Reference Number: X11 (standing) & X11a (kneeling)
Type: single

Method: From a standing position with feet shoulder–width apart, place the hands

slightly behind the hips. Lean back pushing the hips forward. As you breathe out continue arching and allow your hands to drop as far down the legs as they can go before resistance is met.

Points to note:
1. The backward arching will be encouraged if you allow your mouth to relax and open.
2. The gentle thrust forward of your hips will require your buttocks to be clenched.
3. This stretch can be extended (11a) from the kneeling position by working your hands out towards your feet. This has the added advantage of being slightly more easily balanced.

Title: **PELVIC THRUST**
Body Area: CHEST, FRONT THIGH
Reference Number: X12
Type: single

Method: From the lying extended position, flex at the knees and thrust the hips up, supporting them with the arms. Move the heels towards the buttocks.

Points to note:
1. Keep your feet flat on the floor.
2. Use your shoulders to lift you up.

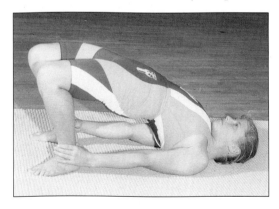

3. As you improve in strength and flexibility you can extend the stretch further by moving the hands further towards the feet and the feet towards the shoulders until they meet.

Title: **HUMAN 'O'**
Body Area: SHOULDERS, CHEST, FRONT THIGH
Reference Number: X13
Type: single

Method: This, in some ways, is X12 the other way up. Lie on your front, reach backwards and grasp the legs around the ankles. Lift the knees and chest off the floor.

Points to note:
1. The stronger and more flexible you get, the further up the feet you can reach.
2. At any position the stretch will be greater the more the knees are kept together.

Title: **HUMPBACK BRIDGE**
Body Area: BACK
Reference Number: X14
Type: single

Method: Kneel and support your weight evenly on all fours. Round the back by lowering the head and contracting the abdominals. Hold the stretch. Relax to flat back position and repeat.

Title: **WAGGLE**
Body Area: SIDES OF TRUNK
Reference Number: X15
Type: double

Method: On all fours lower one shoulder by flexing an arm and then slowly rotate at the hips taking your bottom out to one side. Hold and relax and repeat as usual.

Title: **FLAT TWIST**
Body Area: SIDES OF TRUNK
Reference Number: X16
Type: double

Method: Lie flat on your back with arms stretched out at shoulder height. Keeping shoulders, arms and back of head in contact with the floor draw the legs up together and lower them towards the floor together.

Title: **SAMSON**
Body Area: CHEST PECTORALS
Reference Number: X17 & X17a & X17b
Type: single

Method: In a doorway, forearms vertically against the door posts but elbows lower than shoulders, lean forward by bending the front leg at the knee to achieve the stretch.

Point to note:
1. This exercise can be repeated with the initial arm position first with elbows at shoulder height and then at about ear height to stretch progressively different sections of the pectorals.

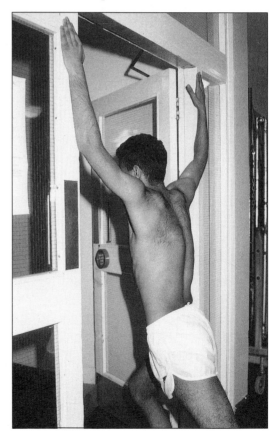

Title: **LEAN TO**
Body Area: TOP OF ARMS, SHOULDERS
Reference Number: X18
Type: single

Method: Standing upright with the back to a wall, arms against the wall at shoulder height, fingers pointing up the wall, lower the shoulders by bending at the knees.

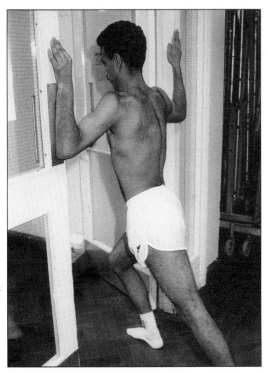

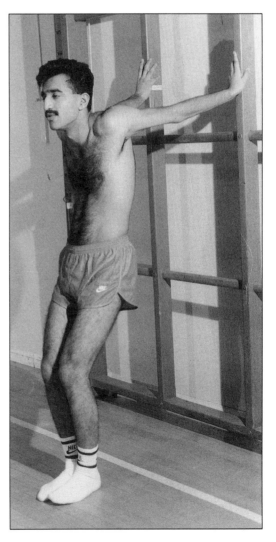

Title: **CREEP**
Body Area: SHOULDERS, ARMS AND BACK
Reference Number: X19
Type: single

Method: On all fours creep the arms forward and lower the chest. Hold and repeat as usual.

Title: **METRONOME**
Body Area: TRUNK SIDES
Reference Number: X20 (straddle) & X20a (sitting)
Type: double

Method: These are two stretches done sitting with legs crossed or in a straddle position. Hands clasped behind the head and elbows high, bring the elbow on one side down towards the knee/floor on the same side. Hold and repeat as usual.

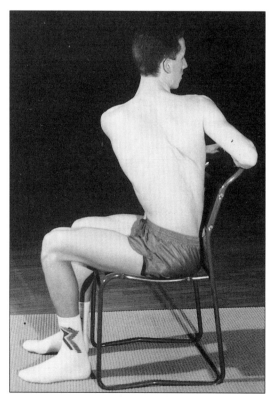

Title: **SIDE TURN**
Body Area: SIDES AND CHEST AND BACK
Reference Number: X21
Type: double

Method: Sitting upright in a firm chair twist the upper body only to one side and place the hands on the back of the chair.

Title: **TORSO TWIST**
Body Area: SIDES OF TRUNK AND SHOULDERS AND PARTS OF BACK AND CHEST
Reference Number: X22
Type: double

Method: Kneel on all fours and lean forward extending the arms as far as possible, letting the chest fall forward towards the floor. Twist the upper trunk to one side pressing down with the forearms and hands.

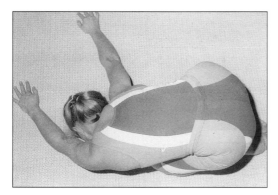

Title: **OVER THE TOP**
Body Area: SHOULDERS AND ARMS
Reference Number: X23 (reverse grip) & X23a (normal grip)
Type: single

Method: Grasping a pole or towel (reverse grip) behind your back, stand upright with legs apart. Raise arms straight and slow over head and down as far as possible.

Points to note:

1. If you start with the normal grip in front and repeat the action from front to over head you get a different stretch.

2. The wider the grip the easier the action and so these stretches have an inbuilt training overload function because as it becomes easy you can make it difficult again.

TO ENHANCE BASIC STRETCHES LOWERS C1–C13

Title: **EXTENDED TOE TOUCH**
Body Area: HAMSTRINGS AND BACK
Reference Number: X24 & X24a
Type: single/double

Method: Stand with feet crossed and slowly drop down to a toe touch (or as far as you can go), keep knees slightly flexed, then straighten at knees.

Point to note:

1. This can then be varied to one side and the other to increase the range of the stretch.

Title: **RIGHT ANGLES**
Body Area: HAMS AND LEG SIDES
Reference Number: X25
Type: double

Method: Lie on your back with one leg raised as near to the vertical as possible. If you cannot make the vertical do not do this exercise. With arms flat at shoulder height, lower raised leg to floor at side keeping it straight.

Title: **SPLITS**
Body Area: HAMSTRINGS OF LEAD LEG AND QUADRICEPS OF TRAILING LEG
Reference Number: X26
Type: double

Method: This is a well-known position, often done incorrectly. With the hip at right angles to the line of the legs, descend slowly. This exercise can be extended

Method: With hips in line with the legs, descend slowly, toes pointed.

Title: **WALL STRADDLE**
Body Area: GROIN
Reference Number: X28 and X28a
Type: single

Method: Simply lie with buttocks against a

with a rolled cloth under the front and/or the back ankle.

Title: **BOX SPLITS**
Body Area: THIGH MUSCLES INNER AND OUTER
Reference Number: X27
Type: double

wall and legs up the wall vertically, then allow the legs to separate as far as possible, but slowly. You can also bend at the knees and bring feet together to reduce the pull from the weight of your legs. Then try to pull your knees right to the wall as well.

Point to note:
1. Variations on this use of the wall with one leg at a time can be done to stretch hamstrings singly.

Title: **DOUBLE LOW CALF**
Body Area: CALF MUSCLES
Reference Number: X29
Type: single

Method: With feet together and heels down, lean against the wall with body straight – take it as low as possible for a powerful stretch. Repeat with knees bent as much as possible but heels down.

Point to note:
1. These are basically the same stretches as seen in C11 and C12 but using both feet together and adding to the stretch with body weight.

TO ENHANCE BASIC STRETCHES EXTREMITIES D1–D4

In these stretches the principle is to add to a passive stretch of fingers, toes, ankle and wrist by introducing a controlled use of body weight to extend the stretch.

Title: **WRIST PUSH**
Body Area: FOREARMS
Reference Number: X30
Type: single

Method: On all fours allow weight to go forward to achieve the stretch.

Title: **ANKLE PUSH**
Body Area: FRONT OF LOWER LEG AND TOES
Reference Number: X31
Type: double

Method: Standing straight, point the forward foot and rest the tops of the toes on the floor, then shift the weight forwards to achieve a stretch.

TO ENHANCE BASIC STRETCHES TOTALS E1–E3

Title: **LEAN AWAY**
Body Area: SIDES
Reference: X32
Type: double

Method: Stand at arms' length from a wall and lean against it through one straight arm. With feet together, pointing parallel to the wall, rotate the hips a little bit forward and then towards the wall, then push with your free hand on the hips to create the stretch.

Point to note:
1. Legs and supporting arm must be straight throughout.

Title: **HANGS**
Body Area: ALL LONG VERTICAL MUSCLES
Reference Number: X33
Type: single

Method: Grasp a bar or the rings and hang, feet just off the floor.

Point to note:
1. This can be reversed by hanging from your feet, but make sure you have a soft landing and do not hold the stretch too long.

8

ADVANCED STRETCHING METHODS (PNF)

Although these types of stretching were originally developed as an element of the medical treatment for physically handicapped patients, they have been adopted by sport even if in a rather bastardized form. There has been a fair amount of criticism over the years from those, mainly physiotherapists, who feel, with some justification, that it has too often become a misused and badly used form of training. This is not so much because it does not work, but more because it has been put in the hands of the untrained who often do not appreciate the real techniques or the dangers associated with badly implementing the processes.

However, these types of stretching are being used and will continue to be used by coaches and sports performers. Consequently, this chapter looks at the proprioceptive neuromuscular facilitation (PNF) technique in the hope that those who are intent on using it will do so more safely having read this section, and it also explains why ballistic stretching is unacceptable.

PROPRIOCEPTIVE NEUROMUSCULAR FACILITATION

The advantages of PNF techniques seem to be that you can make larger gains in the range of motion in a shorter time; muscles exhibit less resistance to movement; strength is gained at the same time as range; and the resultant stability of a joint is enhanced by building a more balanced pull in the muscles involved. The (potential) disadvantages are the increased chance for damage due to an incompetent assistant or partner; the inherently more painful and stressful processes; and the cardiovascular pressures associated with isometric contractions. The building-up of pressure in the chest and abdomen, which can accompany the straining associated with isometrics, can increase stress on the heart and circulation (valsalva phenomenon) and/or burst a weak muscle/tissue layer in the gut (hernia).

PNF can take at least nine different forms, all using different combinations of passive and active stretching as well as isometric and isotonic contractions. Alter (1988) summarizes these methods very well. For our purposes, two strategies will suffice to show what is in common usuage. The two methods are described as they should be conducted and then combined to show how they can form one technique for practical use.

The PNF methods are active and passive; the distinction being essentially in the role of the partner who takes purely a supportive role in active PNF because the subject works his own muscles throughout. Conversely the second form is passive because much of the muscle functioning has been taken on by the partner.

ACTIVE PNF

This is the preferred form because:
a. The partner supports and resists but does not stretch the muscles.
b. The technique includes strength training at the (new) limits of flexibility.

The method can be applied to all muscles, but the hamstring example will be used for this description. Having made sure the muscles have been properly warmed up the subject and partner take up the starting positions as shown on page 124.

The subject starts by contracting the muscles which normally stretch the target muscles. So in this case, the quadriceps start to pull out the hamstrings. This allows reciprocal inhibition (RI) (*see* Chapter 3 on neurophysiology) to take place as it is an active movement and the hamstrings stretch as the leg rises. The activity of the quadriceps initiates an inhibition to the stretch reflex in the hamstrings, so they stretch.

As the resistance to stretch, inherent in the hamstrings, builds up and/or the subject's strength begins to fail to support the leg, then the partner holds the limb at this first limit position.

The subject next contracts the hamstrings against the partner who resists the contraction making it an isometric contraction. The limb is therefore not moved although it is trying to flex because the hamstrings are working hard. The intention is to contract only the muscle which is being trained. The isometric contraction takes place for 10 seconds and in doing so, effects autogenic inhibition (AI) (*see* Chapter 3). The increase in tension occasioned by the contraction stimulates the Golgi tendon organs to cause a reflex relaxation in the hamstrings.

Following the 10 seconds of isometric

contraction by the hamstrings, there is a relaxation and further concentric contraction of the quadriceps by the subject to a new stretched limit where the partner supports again.

The sequence can then be started again with a second isometric contraction of the hamstrings for 10 seconds, followed by a further active lift to the new limit.

As you get better at the technique you will relax more easily and everything will work that much better. The active phase of concentric contraction may even be enhanced in terms of strength training, by either attaching some extra weight to the part being moved or letting the partner semi-resist the contraction. This is really quite advanced technical work and as such is not necessary for the majority of normal sports and sports performers.

PASSIVE PNF

In the passive form, the partner has to be very sensitive to the subject and concentrate hard on feeling the various tensions being created.

Using the same example as above, instead of concentric contraction of the quads by the subject the partner moves the limb so the hamstrings start stretching and resistance is felt, i.e. concentric contraction of the agonist has been replaced by a passive movements of the joint in the agonist path by the partner. If the subject continuously gives verbal feedback to his partner then this will reduce the risk of overstretching. At the point of resistance the partner holds the stretched position and the subject contracts isometrically as before. After 10 seconds the partner takes up the newly formed 'slack' as autogenic inhibition aids the relaxing muscle to be stretched.

The process can now be repeated with the subject being called on for a sequence of isometric contractions and relaxations.

This passive form does not work on the strength of the agonist (quadriceps), but might be used after exercise as an aid to both flexibility and warm-down relaxation. The stretch is likely to go further by extending the passive range. It has a role in connection with, rather than as an alternative to, active PNF. This combined method seems the most practical and useful way of using PNF and is described below.

The difference between the two methods or procedures is that the active method allows the agonist to be strengthened by concentric contractions and the antagonist to be strengthened by isometric contractions. The passive method allows only the antagonist to be strengthened by isometric contractions.

COMBINED PNF

In the real world good training and competition has as much to do with motivation as it does with anything else. By sensitively combining the passive with the active your partner/coach can take the human situations of fatigue and demotivation into account.

As we have seen, the active process may be best for dynamic flexibility but, after an initial active phase, the partner can aid a further stretch in the same way a buddy in the weights room helps you through your last couple of repeats in the final set of lifts. That is, adding the last 1 per cent or 2 per cent to the efforts of the subject, allowing work at the extreme end of his or her range. This really does require sensitivity and feel on behalf of the partner and trust on behalf of the subject.

The combined method allows the training to gain both strength and flexibility by incorporating both RI and AI but in the realistic framework of needing motivation and assistance when working at extremes. As with all stretches once you have worked both of the hamstrings then you would work a stretch on the quadriceps. In PNF style this would require a partner-assisted version of C8 or C9 (see Chapter 7) where in this case the active method requires the hamstrings to be worked concentrically and the quadriceps, being stretched, worked isometrically.

Although PNF is normally a partner activity some stretches can be achieved by yourself but still in PNF form. With some stretches you can use, say, one arm as the resistance to the isometric contraction and then move in the same way that a partner might act. Equally it is possible to use objects like tables or walls to support a contraction and to stretch the relaxed muscle. This may be preferable as you are taking fuller personal control of the exercise. The dedicated student of sport might wish to follow up on this brief and limited explanation of PNF by making reference to Cornelius and Hinson (1980), Hardy (1985), Hartley O'Brien (1980), Knott and Voss (1968), Prentice (1983), Sullivan, Markos and Minor (1982), Surburg (1981) and, of course, Alter (1988). The work done by Prentice rather indicated that stretching with PNF for the same period as SASS gave only comparatively little advantage, so for most of the effort of learning and doing PNF seems dubious.

Before moving on to look at ballistic stretching it is important to emphasize the safety points in PNF.

PNF SAFETY FIRST

1. SASS works and therefore (as far as sport, as opposed to medicine, is concerned) PNF is unnecessary. So do not bother to use PNF unless you need to:
a. work on a particularly stiff area to bring it into balance with the other muscles;
b. become involved in a particularly demanding sport from the point of view of flexibility and must work at the extremes;
c. gain flexibility more quickly than SASS allows.
2. Do not allow just anyone to be your partner/assistant. Check they know exactly what they are doing. Try to stick to the same partner.
3. Always use (and make sure your partner uses on you) slow and minimum force actions for all the passive stretching parts.
4. You, as the subject, should control the duration, intensity and frequency of PNF work and are always the final arbiter on when it stops.
5. Pain, as you, not your partner or coach, define it, is never part of this training. If it is pain you are feeling, then you are, or are about to be, damaging tissue.
6. The requirements of relaxation and warm tissue are just as, if not even more, crucial to the practice of PNF as they are to SASS.
7. SASS can be combined with PNF.
8. 'Geeing up' for competition in flexibility or any form of 'going for it' mentality is always wrong.
9. How flexible you were yesterday or last week is not directly related to how flexible you are today. Flexibility varies through the day too. If you cannot express the flexibility you showed previously, do not alter your method or break the rules. Tomorrow it may be better again.

BALLISTIC STRETCHING

Ballistic stretching uses repetitive contractions of the agonistic muscle to give hard, fast stretches to the antagonist muscle. Thus jerks and pulls are used in an attempt to increase flexibility. Ballistic stretching is out of control passive stretching.

There are no occasions when ballistic (dynamic or bouncing) type stretching should be used to train for flexibility. Yet by observation it seems the most frequent method used by performers when they are preparing to be active. This is because:
a. it is easy to do, there is a rhythm to it;
b. it is more like 'real' training – dynamic;
c. lots of people do it;
d. it feels as if you are getting to your maximum.

The ballistic principle uses repetitive contractions of the agonist muscle, often aided by gravity, to give fast, hard jerks to the antagonist muscles, and so stretch them and the connective tissue associated with them.

The most easy example is to imagine repetitive toe touches from the standing position. The subject pulls the top half of the body down and gravity increases the momentum until the tissue of the hamstrings are overstretched and elasticity of fibres, together with the stretch reflex, exert enough tension to recoil the thrust. The stretch reflex must act against the stretch because there is no time for the inverse reflex to be initiated (*see* Chapter 3, section on neurophysiology). It is basically, or at least often, a passive movement in that the initial agonist contraction which might, through RI, suppress the stretch reflex, if it occurs at all, ceases immediately after starting the motion.

Even if the stretch reflex has been suppressed, this does not help because the speed and force of the bounce takes over and the joint must rely on its own supportive tissue to stop the motion. If the tissue is stretched in this way then once the extensibility of that tissue is exceeded the fibres will be damaged.

It is easy to think you are doing a safe stretch and to let bouncing creep in. The test is to make sure you can stop and then maintain that position at any time – there must not be any momentum taking you on. If part of the body is flung and then muscles relax, the result will always be a ballistic movement. This is particularly easy to do in movement to music situations where the rhythm and ambience can take over, relaxing the protective devices and leaving the subject vulnerable to continuous damaging forces.

Ballistic stretching tends to increase muscle soreness whereas SASS tends to reduce and relieve such pains. It is no accident that the normal procedure used by sports players to relieve cramp is a slow stretching out of that muscle. De Vries (1986) gives the classical background to all this.

In sport there are a lot of ballistic movements like kicking, swinging bats and throwing, but these are safe when they are kept within the limits of an athlete's normal dynamic range of flexibilities. They are also usually associated with 'triggers' which slow the movement down. The example given earlier of the contact with the ball in a kick being a 'trigger' to start using the opposite muscle to slow the foot down and protect the knee, is a good one (*see* Chapter 3, neurophysiology section). In the unforeseen overstretch situation which must occur in active sports it will be the 'buffer zone' of static flexibility gained in training that will protect the joint. Bouncing or ballistics is never the way to achieve maximum static and dynamic flexibilities.

REFERENCES

Alter, M. J., *Science of Stretching*, Human Kinetics, 1988

Cornelius, W. L. and Hinson, M. M., 'The Relationship Between Isometric Contractions of Hip Extensions and Subsequent Flexibility in Males', *Journal of Sports Medicine* 20: pp75–80, 1980

Etynre, B. R. and Lee, E. J., 'Comments on PNF Stretching Techniques', *Research Quarterly* 58(2): pp184–8, 1987

Etynre, B. R. and Abraham, L. D., 'Antagonistic Muscle Activity During Stretching', *PA Medicine and Science in Sports and Exercise* 20(3): p285, 1988

Hardy, L., 'Improving Active Range of Hip Flexion', *Research Quarterly* 56(2): pp111–14, 1985

Hardy, L. and Jones, D., 'Dynamic Flexibility and PNF', *Research Quarterly* 57(2) : pp150–3, 1986

Hartley-O'Brien, S. J., 'Six Mobilization Exercises for Active Range of Hip Flexion', *Research Quarterly* 51(4): pp625–5, 1980

Knott, M. and Voss, D. E., *Proprioceptive Neuromuscular Facilitation: Patterns and Techniques*, Harper and Row, 1968

Lucas, R. C. and Koslow, R., 'Comparative Study of Static, Dynamic and PNF Stretching Techniques on Flexibility Perceptual and Motor Skills' 58: pp615–18, 1984

Prentice, W., 'Comparison of Static Stretching and PNF Stretching for Improved Hip Joint Flexibility', *Athletic Training* 18: pp56–9, 1983

Roundtable, 'Flexibility', *National Strength and Conditioning Association* 6(4): p10, 1984

Sady, S. P., Wortman, H. and Blanke, D., 'Flexibility Training: Ballistic, Static or PNF', *Arch, Phys. Med. Rehabil* 63: pp261–3, 1982

Sullivan, P. D., Markos, P. E. and Minor, M. D., *An Integrated Approach to Therapeutic Exercise Theory and Clinical Application*, Reston Publishing, 1982

Surburg, P. R., 'Neuromuscular Facilitation Techniques in Sports Medicine', *Physician and Sports Medicine* 9 (1), pp114–27, 1981

Williford, H. N. and Smith, J. F., 'A Comparison of PNF and Static Stretching Techniques', *American Corrective Therapy Journal* 39(2): pp30–33, 1985

9

ADVANCED STRETCHING EXERCISES (PNF)

This final section of stretches is to give the seeker of extremes in flexibility some examples of the assisted stretches which could be added to their programme.

In many cases the PNF stretches can be done with or without a partner, by using a solid object or your own muscles to achieve a safe and effective PNF stretch. The SASS stretches can be the basic starting point and then they can be enhanced by resisting and supporting as necessary. For example, the C4 groin stretch can become PNF by using the elbows to resist contractions and push to new stretch.

This section is by no means exhaustive but is meant to give a few examples. If you apply the rules as already discussed there are plenty of other stretches which can be invented. The most comprehensive single source of exercises is the *Science of Stretching* by Alter (1988).

As stated earlier, it is not appropriate to simply say these are the exercises a particular sport requires; indeed, you should address your own personal and individual

The first example shows the gradual nature of the stretch with the partner supporting at each stage as the stretch increases. **Use the method outlined in the PNF section** for preference with the active rather than passive system.

The remaining pictures are given as examples but without names or references. In the majority of cases it will be clear which basic stretches are being extended through the use of PNF.

limitations by picking the exercises which will work on those weaknesses. Always remember to balance your programme by not working on one area or side to the exclusion of another.

REMEMBER

These stretches are not necessary nor are they recommended for the vast majority of sports or sports performers.

These stretches must be conducted either by yourself (where appropriate) or with an experienced and totally trusted assistant/coach.

These stretches are by their nature potentially injury producing.

The following photos show ways in which a partner can assist a stretch. It may look as if the partner is pulling but the real job is to resist and support with a minimum of pushing.

REFERENCES

Alter, M. J., *Science of Stretching*, Human kinetics, 1988

Knott, M. and Voss, D. E., *Proprioceptive Neuromuscular Facilitation: Patterns and Techniques*, Harper and Row, 1968

Surburg, P. R., 'Neuromuscular Facilitation Techniques in Sportsmedicine', *Physician and Sportsmedicine* 9(1), pp. 114–27, 1981

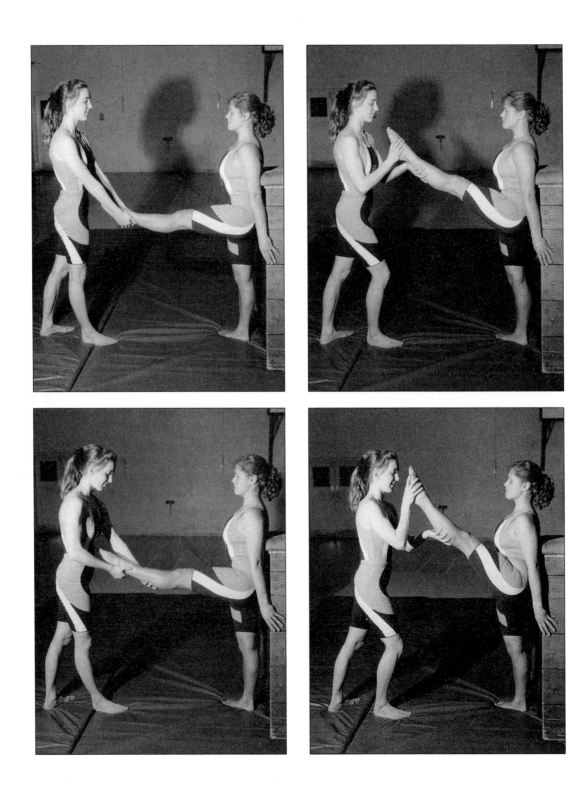

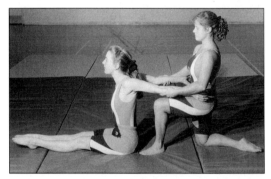

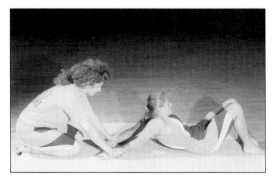

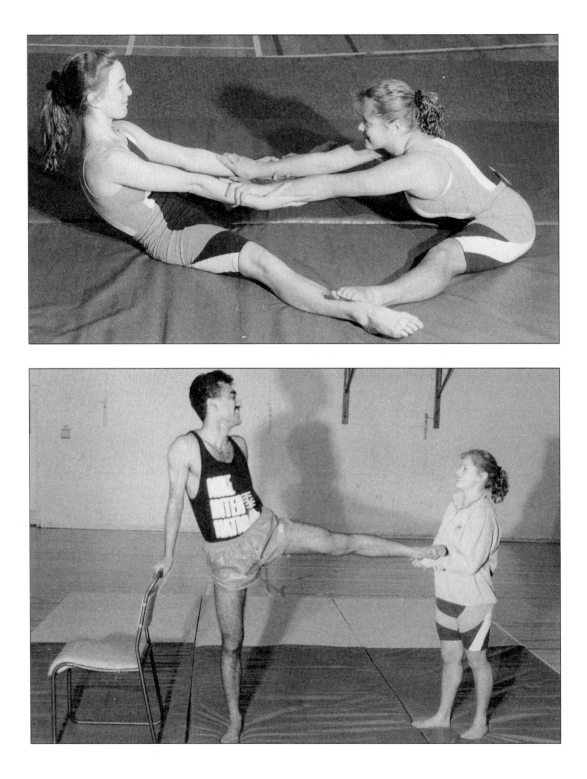

PART THREE

GLOSSARY

This section gives definitions of terms which may have been less than fully defined within the text. I have used primarily adapted definitions which have their origin in the worthy text *The Sports Science Handbook* by Simon Jenkins (1990).

adhesion unwanted cross linkages in connective tissue associated with collagen. Reduces range of motion.

aerobic oxygen using (energy production). Associated with endurance activities like long and middle distance, road cycling etc.

anaerobic without using oxygen (energy production). Associated with power and sprint activities like 100 metres, golf and weight lifting.

atlas the first cervical vertebra.

autogenic inhibition overcoming the stretch reflex in the muscle being stretched by an isometric contraction of that muscle, which stimulates the Golgi tendon organs to effect the relaxation. Thus this involves the Inverse Stretch Reflex.

axis   the second cervical vertebra.

ball and socket joint   the rounded head of a bone articulates with the cavity of another, e.g. hip or shoulder joint.

ballistic stretch/movement   any motion although initiated by muscular activity which is allowed to continue under its own momentum without muscular control.

biarticulate muscle   any muscle that crosses two joints, e.g. calf muscle, gastrocnemius.

biochemistry   the study of the chemistry of living things.

biomechanics   the study of human movements through the application of mechanical theory.

blood pressure   the pressures acting in the arteries. The highest being when the ventricles of the heart contract (systole) and the lowest when the ventricles have relaxed (diastole).

cartilage   a form of connective tissue which contains no blood vessels. There are two types of cartilage associated with movement:
a. hyaline – elastic, containing no nerves. Found on joint surfaces and in immature bones before calcification.
b. white fibro – tough, flexible and elastic tissue acting as shock absorbers and movement enhancers, e.g. menisci of the knee.

circumduction   movement which allows the end of a limb, or other part, to describe a circle. A combination of flexion, abduction, adduction and extension.

collagen   a fibrous protein which is the major component of some connective tissues like ligaments.

connective tissue   a group name for tissues which are connective or supporting, e.g. bone, cartilage, ligaments, joint capsule and tendon.

elasticity   physical property of being able to be stretched and returned to its original length.

endurance   longer term, submaximal activity. The time limit of an individual's ability to maintain either a specific power output or a specific isometric force.

epiphyseal   pertaining to the cartilage discs at the end of growing bones, which calcify during maturation.

extension   a movement which increases the angle between two bones. (*See* hyperextension.)

fascia   a. superficial – fat filled layer of fibrous tissue connecting the skin to the deeper fascia.
b. deep – dense elastic tissue encasing blood vessels, nerves and muscles.

flexibility   the range of non-pathological movement around a joint or series of joints. It is determined by the architecture of the skeleton, the length (or effective) length of muscles and tendons and the resistance of other tissues associated with the joint.
a. static – the degree a joint can be moved passively.
b. dynamic – the degree a joint can be moved actively.

flexion   a movement decreasing the angle between two bones.

hyperflexibility   (hypermobility) excessive flexibility. loose or lax connective tissue of a joint or series of joints resulting in an inability to limit associated movements. This pathological state can be associated with excessive, intense mobility training which has occurred to immature bodies, i.e. prior to the calcification of the epiphyseal growth plates.

hypoflexibility   (hypomobility)   lack of normal flexibility. A stiffness or tightness of connective tissue of a joint or series of joints.

hyperextension extension beyond 180 degrees.

inverse stretch reflex if a muscle is held in a stretched position for at least six seconds then the Golgi tendon organs respond to the stretch by initiating impulses which override the stretch reflex, allowing the stretched muscle to relax.

joint capsule a sleeve of connective tissue that surrounds the ends of the two bones in a synovial joint.

ligaments strong bands of special connective tissue which connect bones and restrict movements to a specific range. They are pliant and flexible yet relatively inelastic.

movement changes in joint angles and/ or changes in the position of the whole body.

muscle spindles sense organs in skeletal muscle stimulated by muscle stretch. Important in the stretch reflex.

plyometrics a type of training aimed at increasing power. It relies on the assertion that pre-stretching a muscle before it contracts increasing the subsequent contraction. Depth jumping is the commonest example.

plantar flexion the movement of pushing the toes down as in thrusting off or pointing the toes.

stretch reflex (myotatic reflex) stretching a muscle stretches the muscle spindles which initiates vollies of impulses to the spinal cord which in turn stimulates the stretched muscle to contract.

synovial joint (diathrosis) a joint containing synovial membrane and fluid, enclosed in a capsule of connective tissue. The articular cartilage of the joint is lined with the synovial membrane which secretes the nutritous synovial fluid.

tendon inelastic cords of fibrous connective tissue which join muscles to bones, ligament or other connective tissue.

training a thought-out programme of activities designed to assist improvement of fitness and/or skill levels.

viscoelastic physical property of a solid or liquid which allows it to store and dissipate energy during mechanical deformation.

viscosity the friction within a fluid.

BIBLIOGRAPHY

Listed here are all the books, articles, etc., which have been consulted in the preparation of this book, together with a number of sports science or related texts useful to those who wish to study more about exercise.

The literature has been grouped in sections so that the reader can focus on a particular area. However, in the nature of such things, it is difficult to make this classification totally exclusive and there is an inevitable overlap. Where the overlap seemed particularly large the particular text may have been cited more than once.

Although the majority of the material has something to recommend it, there are of course ideas and suggestions in some books or articles with which it would not always be possible to concur. In respect to the flexibility work, before accepting a suggested stretch or exercise as appropriate, the reader should apply the criteria of good practice discussed through this book and then make their own judgement.

GENERAL BIOLOGY, ANATOMY AND PHYSIOLOGY OF EXERCISE

Anthony, C. and Thibodeau, G., *Structure and Function of the Body*, 6th edn, Mosby (St Louis), 1980

★Astrand, P-O. and Rodahl, K., *Textbook of Work Physiology: Physiological Bases of Exercise*, 3rd edn, McGraw-Hill, 1988

★de Vries, H. A., *Physiology of Exercise*, 4th edn, Brown & Co. (USA), 1986

★Fox, E. L., *Sports Physiology*, W. B. Saunders Co. (Philadelphia), 1984

Green, J., *An Introduction to Human Physiology*, 4th edn, Oxford University Press, 1978

★McArdle, W., Katch, F. and Katch, V., *Exercise Physiology: Energy, Nutrition and Human Performance*, Lea & Febiger, 1986

★McNaught-Davis, J. P., *Developing Flexibility* (Resource Pack), National Coaching Foundation, 1986

★NCF Coaching Handbook 3, *Physiology and Performance*, National Coaching Foundation, 1988

★Powers, S. K. and Howley, E. T., *Exercise Physiology: Theory and Application to Fitness and Performance*, Wm. C. Brown (Iowa), 1990

Tortora, G. J. and Anagnostakos, N. P., *Principles of Anatomy and Physiology*, 3rd edn, Harper Row, 1982

Vander, A. J., Sherman, J. H. and Luciano, D. S., *Human Physiology: The Mechanisms of Body Function*, 4th edn, McGraw-Hill, 1985

Warwick, R. and Williams, P. L., *Gray's Anatomy*, 35th edn, Longman, 1973

★Woods, B., *Structure of the Body* (Resource Pack), National Coaching Foundation, 1990

★Exercise science specific sources

SPORTS PSYCHOLOGY

Albinson, J. G. and Bull, S. J., *A Mental Game Plan*, Spondyn, 1988

Bull, S. J., *Personal and Situational Influences on Adherence to Mental Skills Training*, paper given at the British Association of Sports Sciences Conference, 13–15 September 1990

Harris, D. V. and Harris, B. L., *The Athletes Guide to Sports Psychology*, Human Kinetics, Champaign, Illinois, 1984.

Terry, P., *The Winning Mind*, Thorsons, 1989

EXERCISE AND HEALTH

Armstrong, N., Balding, J., Bray, S., Gentle, P. and Kirby, B., *The Physical Activity Patterns of 10 and 13 Year Old Children*, paper given at 14th International Seminar on Pediatric Work Physiology, Leuven, Belgium, 1989

Astrand, P-O., *Health and Fitness*, Skandia Insurance Company Ltd, Stockholm, 1978

Eassom, S., 'The Myth of Fitness: A Critical Commentary on the Nation's Health', from *Leisure, Labour and Lifestyles International Comparisons*, Vol II: *Leisure and the Quality of Life: Themes and Issues*, edited by Tomlinson, A., LSA Conference Papers No. 42, pp74–87, 1990

McNaught-Davis, J. P., 'Health-related Fitness vs. Health-related Leisure', from *Leisure, Labour and Lifestyles: International Comparisons*, Vol II: *Leisure and the Quality of Life: Themes and Issues*, edited by Tomlinson, A., LSA Conference Papers No. 42, pp67–73, 1990

Workshop Report, Recreation management, *Working out . . . at Work*, The Sports Council National Seminar and Exhibition, 22–4 March 1988

SPORTS SCIENCE AND COACHING

Adams, G., *Designing a Fitness Training Programme*, National Coaching Foundation, 1986

Allsen, P. E., *Conditioning and Physical Fitness – Current Answers to Relevant Questions*, Wm. C. Brown (Iowa), 1978

Corbin, B. C. and Lindsey, R., *Concepts of Physical Fitness*, 5th edn, Wm. C. Brown (Iowa), 1985

Dick, F. W., *Sports Training Principles*, Lepus, 1980

Dick, F. W., *Training Theory*, 2nd edn, BAAB, 1984

Harre, D., *Principles of Sports Training*, Sportverlag (Berlin), 1982

Jenkins, S. P. R., *Sports Science Handbook*, Sunningdale, 1990

McNaught-Davis, J. P. and McFee, G., Accreditation for a post-graduate profession, in *Coach Education: Preparation for a Profession*. The

proceedings of the VIII Commonwealth and International Conference on Sport, Physical Education, Dance, Recreation and Health. Glasgow 18–23 July 1986. London: Spon. 1986

Morehouse, L. E. and Rasch, P. J., *Scientific Basis of all Training*, W. B. Saunders, 1958

NCF Coaching Focus, *Strength, Speed and Power*, National Coaching Foundation, February 1988

Sports Council, *Annual Report, 1978–9*, (Sport for All)

Sports Council, *Annual Report, 1982–3*, (NCF decision September 1982)

Sports Council, *Annual Report, 1983–4*, (NCF first report)

Taylor, A. W., *The Scientific Aspects of Sports Training*, Charles C. Thomas, 1975

Wilmore, J. H., *Athletic Training and Physical Fitness: Physiological Principles and Practices of the Conditioning Process*, Allyn & Bacon (Boston), 1977

Wirhed, R., *Athletic Ability and the Anatomy of Motion*, Wolfe Medical Publishing, 1985

FLEXIBILITY TEXTS AND STRETCHING PROGRAMMES

Anderson, B., *Stretching*, Pelham Books, 1980

Allsen, P. E., *Conditioning and Physical Fitness – Current Answers to Relevant Questions*, Wm. C. Brown (Iowa), 1978

Alter, M. J., *Science of Stretching*, Human Kinetics, 1988

Beaulieu, J. E., *Stretching for all Sports,* The Athletic Press (California), 1980

Connolly, C. and Einzig, H., *The Fitness Jungle – Stage 2, The Exercise Survival Guide,* Century, 1986

Hubley, C., 'Testing Flexibility', from *Physiological Testing of the Elite Athlete,* edited by MacDougall, J. D., Wenger, M. A. and Green, H. J., Movement Publishers (New York), 1982

McNaught-Davis, J. P., *Developing Flexibility* (Resource Pack), National Coaching Foundation, 1986

McNaught-Davis, J. P., *Developing Flexibility* (Video), Brighton Polytechnic, Media Services, Watts Bld., Brighton, £40 inc. p&p

Russell, K., *Increasing Joint Range of Movement in Young Athletes,* paper presented to British Association of National Coaches, Birmingham, December 1985

Smith, A., *The Total Fitness Program – Stretch,* Acropolis Books (Washington), 1983

FLEXIBILITY AND RELATED ARTICLES

(Mainly research articles)

Atha, J. and Wheatley, D. W., 'The Mobilising Effects of Repeated Measurement on Hip Flexion', *British Journal of Sports Medicine* 10(1): pp. 22–5, 1976

Aura, O. and Komi, P. V., 'Effects of Prestretch Intensity on Mechanical Efficiency of Positive Work and on Elastic Behaviour of Skeletal Muscle in Stretch-shortening Cycle Exercises', *International Journal of Sports Medicine* 7: pp137–43, 1986

Benjamin, B. and Roth, P., 'Warming Up vs. Stretching', *Running Times* 34: pp 15–21, November 1979

Beaulieu, J. E., 'Developing a Stretching Program', *The Physician and Sportsmedicine* 9(11): pp59–69, 1981

Borms, J., 'Importance of Flexibility in Overall Physical Fitness', *International Journal of Physical Education* 21(2): pp15–26, 1984

Borms, J., Van Roy, P., Santens, J-P, and Haentjens, A., 'Optimal Duration of Static Stretching Exercises for Improvement of Coxofemoral Flexibility', *Journal of Sport Sciences* 5: pp39–47, 1987

Bosco, C., 'The effect of Pre-stretch on Mechanical Efficiency of Human Skeletal Muscle', *ACTA Physiology Scand* 131: pp323–9

Corbin, C. B. and Noble, L., 'Flexibility – A Major Component of Physical Fitness', *Journal of Physical Education and Recreation 51(6),* pp23–61, June 1980

Cornelius, W. L. and Craft-Hamm, K., 'PNF Flexibility Techniques: Acute Effects on Arterial Blood Pressure', *Physician and Sports Medicine* 16(4): pp152–61, 1988

Cornelius, W. L., Hagemann, R. W. and Jackson, A. W., 'A Study on Placement of Stretching within a Workout', *Journal of Sports Medicine & Physical Fitness* 28(3): pp234–6, 1988

Cornelius, W. L. and Hinson, M. M., 'The Relationship Between Isometric Contractions of Hip Extensors and Subsequent Flexibility in

Males', *Journal of Sports Medicine and Physical Fitness* 20(1), pp 75–80, 1980

de Vries, H. A., 'Evaluation of Static Stretching Procedures for Improvement of Flexibility', *Research Quarterly* 33(2), pp222–8, 1962

Dintiman, G. B., 'Effect of Various Training Programmes on Running Speed', *Research Quarterly* 35: pp456–63, 1964

Docherty, D. and Bell, R. D., 'The Relationship Between Flexibility and Linearity Measures in Boys and Girls 6–15 Years of Age', *Journal of Human Movement Studies* 11: pp279–88, 1985

Etynre, B. R. and Abraham, L. D., 'Antagonistic Muscle Activity During Stretching', *A PA Medical Science Sports Exercises* 20(3): pp285, 1988

Etynre, B. R. and Lee, R. J., 'Chronic and Acute Flexibility of Men and Women Using Three Different Stretching Techniques', *Research Quarterly* 59(3): pp222–8, 1988

Etynre, B. R. and Lee, E. J., 'Comments on PNF Stretching Techniques', *Research Quarterly* 58(2): pp184–8, 1987

Gabbard, C. and Tandy, R., 'Body Conditioning and Flexibility Among Prepubescent Males and Females', *Journal of Human Movement Studies* 14: pp153–9, 1988

Hardy, L., 'Improving Active Range of Hip Flexion', *Research Quarterly* 56(2): pp111–14, 1985

Hardy, L. and Jones, D., 'Dynamic Flexibility and PNF', *Research Quarterly* 57(2): pp150–3, 1986

Harris, M. L., 'A Factor Analytic Study of Flexibility', *Research Quarterly* 40(1): pp62–70, 1969

Hartley-O'Brien, S. J., 'Six Mobilization Exercises for Active Range of Hip Flexion', *Research Quarterly* 51(4): pp625–35, 1980

Hortobagyi, T., Faludi, J., Tihanyi, J. and Merkely, B., 'Effects of Intense "Stretching" – Flexibility Training in the Mechanical Profile of the Knee Extensors and the Range of Motion of the Hip Joint', *International Journal of Sports Medicine* 6: pp317–21, 1985

Jackson, A. W. and Baker, A. A., 'The Relationship of the Sit-and-Reach Text to Criterion Measures of Hamstring and Back Flexibility in Young Females', *Research Quarterly* 57(3): pp183–6, 1986

Jones, D. A., Rutherford, O. M. and Parker, D. F., 'Physiological Changes in Skeletal Muscle as a Result of Strength Training', *Quarterly Journal Experimental Physiology* 74: pp233–56, 1989

Knott, M. and Voss, D. E., *Proprioceptive Neuromuscular Facilitation: Patterns and Techniques*, Harper and Row, 1968

Koch, B. M., Galioto, F. M., Vaccaro, P., Vaccaro, J. and Buckenmyer, P. J., 'Flexibility and Strength Measures in Children Participating in a Cardia Rehabilitation Exercise Program', *Physician and Sports Medicine* 16(2): pp139–47, 1988

Koslow, R. E., 'Bilateral Flexibility in the Upper and Lower Extremities as Related to Age and Gender', *Journal of Human Movement Studies* 13: pp467–72, 1987

Levine, M., Lombardo, J., McNeeley, J. and Anderson, T., 'An Analysis of Individual Stretching Programs of Inter-collegiate Athletes', *Physician and Sports Medicine* 15(3): pp132–6, 1987

Liemohn, W., 'Flexibility and Muscular Strength', *Journal of Physical Education, Recreation and Dance* ((7): pp37–40, 1988

Lucas, R. C. and Koslow, R., 'Comparative Study of Static, Dynamic and PNF Stretching Techniques on Flexibility Perceptual and Motor Skills', 58: pp615–18, 1984

Massey, B. A. and Chaudet, N. L., 'Effects of Systematic Heavy Resistance Exercise on Range of Joint Movement in Young Male Adults', *Research Quarterly* 27(1), pp41–51, 1956

McNaught-Davis, J. P., Goodway, J. D. and White, J., 'Training and Injury in Female Gymnastics', in the Proceedings of the International Congress on Youth, Leisure and Physical Activity and Kinanthropometry IV, 1990

Meyers, E. J., 'Effect of Selected Exercise Variables on Ligament Stability and Flexibility of the Knee', *Research Quarterly* 42(4): pp411–22, 1971

Moore, M. A. and Hutton, R. S., 'Electromyographic Investigation of Muscle Stretching Techniques', *Medicine and Science in Sports and Exercise* 12(5): pp322–9, 1980

Nehrer, S., 'Comparative Investigation of Hip Joint Mobility in the Different Sports of Swimming, Cycling and Running', *Oesterreichisches Journal Fuer Sport-Medizin* 16(1): pp23–9, 1988

Patton, R. W. and Newby, C. L., 'The Relationship of Horizontal Vertebral Movements to Sit and Reach Measures of Flexibility', *American Corrective Therapy Journal* 41(3): pp73–6, 1987

Prentice, W., 'Comparison of Static Stretching and PNF Stretching for Improved Hip Joint Flexibility', *Athletic Training* 18: pp56–9, 1983

Roundtable, 'Flexibility', *National Strength and Conditioning Association* 6(4): p10, 1984

Sady, S. P., Wortman, H. and Blanke, D., 'Flexibility Training: Ballistic, Static or PNF', *Arch. Physiology Medicine Rehabilitation* 63: pp261–3, 1982

Sapega, A., Quendenfeld, T. C., Moyer, R. A. and Butler, R. A., 'Biophysical Factors in Range-of-Motion Exercise', *Physician and Medicine* 9(12): pp57–65, 1981

Schultz, P., 'Flexibility: Day of the Static Stretch', *Physician and Sportsmedicine*, 7(11): pp109–17, 1979

Stamford, B., 'Flexibility and Stretching', *Physician and Sportsmedicine* 12(2): p171, 1984

Surburg, P. R., 'Flexibility Exercise Reexamined', *Athletic Training* 18(1), pp37–40, 1983

Surburg, P. R., 'Neuromuscular Facilitation Techniques in Sportsmedicine', *Physician and Sportsmedicine* (1): pp114–27, 1981

Wilktorssohn-Möller, M., Oberg, B., Ekstrand, J. and Gillquist, J., 'Effects of Warming up, Massage and Stretching on Range of Motion and Muscle Strength in the Lower Extremity', *American Journal of Sports Medicine* 11(4): pp249–52, 1983

Williford, H. N., East, J. B., Smith, F. H. and Burry, L. A., 'Evaluation of Warm-up for Improvement in Flexibility', *American Journal of Sports Medicine* 14(4): pp316–19, 1986

Williford, H. N. and Smith, J. F., 'A Comparison of PNF and Static Stretching Techniques', *American Corrective Therapy Journal* 39(2): pp30–33, 1985

INJURY AND FLEXIBILITY

Barnes, L., 'Preadolescent Training – How Young is Too Young?', *Physician and Sportsmedicine* 7(10), 1979

Basmajian, J. V. (editor), *Therapeutic Exercise* 4th edn, Williams & Wilkins, 1984

Beck, J. L. and Day, R. W., 'Overuse Injuries', *Clinics in Sports Medicine* 4(3): pp553–73, 1985

Bergeron, J. D. and Greene, H. W., *Coaches' Guide to Sport Injuries,* Human Kinetics, 1989

Brobeck, J. R. (editor), *Best and Taylor's Physiological Basis of Medical Practice,* 10th edn, Williams & Wilkins, 1980

Caine, D. J. and Lindner, K. J., 'Overuse Injuries of Growing Bones: The Young Female Gymnast at Risk?', *Physician and Sportsmedicine* 13(12): pp51–64

Chang, D. E., Bushbacher, L. P. and Edlich, R. F., 'Limited Joint Mobility in Power Lifters', *American Journal of Sports Medicine* 16(3): pp280–4, 1988

Ciullo, J. V. and Jackson, D. W., 'Pars Interarticularis Stress Reaction, Spondylolysis and Spondylolisthesis in Gymnasts', *Clinic in Sports Medicine* 4(1), pp95–110, 1985

Ekstrand, J. and Gillquist, J., 'The Frequency of Muscle Tightness and Injuries in Soccer Players', *American Journal of Sports Medicine* 10: pp75–8, 1982

Gardiner, M. D., *The Principles of Exercise Therapy,* 4th edn, Bell & Hyman, 1983

Goodway, J. D., 'Injury in Gymnastics – The Practical Implications', *Gymnast Magazine*, Technical Supplement, May/June 1988

Goodway, J. D., McNaught-Davis, J. P. and White, J., 'The Distribution of Injuries Among Young Female Gymnasts in Relation to Selected Training and Environmental Factors', from *Children and Exercise XIV* edited by G. Beunen et al, Band 4 Schriftenreihe der Hamburg-Mannheimer-Stiftung fur Informationsmedizin, Enke Verlag, 1989

Greipp, J. F., 'Swimmer's Shoulder: The Influence of Flexibility and Weight Training', *Physician and Sportsmedicine* 13(8): pp92–105, 1985

Jenkins, S. P. R. and McNaught-Davis, J. P., *Injuries and Fitness of Elite Golf Professionals.* (1991). Sunningdale Publications, 1 Hamilton Drive, Sunningdale, Berkshire.

Kibler, W. B., Henny, C. C. and McQueen, C., 'Evaluation of Fitness Levels and Injury Patterns in Elite Junior Tennis Players', *Medicine and Science in Sports and Exercises* 18(S24), 1986

Kirby, R. L. et al., 'Flexibility and Musculoskeletal Symptomatology in Female Gymnasts and Age-

Matched Controls', *American Journal of Sports Medicine* 9: pp160–4, 1981

Larson, R. L., 'Epiphyseal Injuries in the Adolescent Athlete', *Orthopaedic Clinics in North America* 4: pp839–51, 1973

Lubell, A., 'Potentially Dangerous Exercises: Are They Harmful to All?', *Physician and Sportsmedicine* 17(1) pp187–92, 1989

Micheli, L. J., A Round Table, 'Sports in Childhood', *Physician and Sportsmedicine,* 10(8): pp52–60

Moretz, J. A., Walters, R. and Smith, L., 'Flexibility as a Predictor of Knee Injuries in College Football Players', *Physician and Sportsmedicine* 10(7): pp93–7, 1982

Moynes, D. R., 'Prevention of Injury to the Shoulder Through Exercises and Therapy', *Clinics in Sports Medicine* 2(2): pp413–22, 1983

Peterson, L. and Renstrom, P., *Sports Injuries,* Dunitz, 1986

Reid, D. C., Burnham, R. S., Saboe, L. A. and Kushner, S. F., 'Lower Extremity Flexibility Patterns in Classical Ballet Dancers and their Correlations to Lateral Hip and Knee Injuries', *American Journal of Sports Medicine* 15(4): pp347–52, 1987

Reilly, T., *Sports Fitness and Sports Injuries,* Faber & Faber, 1981

Renstrom, P. and Peterson, L., 'Groin Injuries in Athletes', *British Journal of Sports Medicine* 14: pp30–6, 1980

Shellock, F. G. and Prentice, W. E., 'Warming-up and Stretching for Improved Physical Performance and Prevention of Sports-related Injuries', *Sports Medicine* 2: pp267–78, 1985

Steele, V. A. and White, J. A., 'Injury Amongst Female Gymnasts', proceedings of the Society of Sports Sciences: Sport and Science Conference, Liverpool, 1983

Steele, V. A. and White, J. A., 'Injury Prediction in Female Gymnasts', *British Journal of Sports Medicine* 20: pp31–3

Steiner, M. E., Grana, W. A., Chillag, K. and Schelberg-Karnes, E., 'The Effect of Exercise on Anterior-Posterior Knee Laxity', *American Journal of Sports Medicine* 14(1): pp24–9, 1986

Steiner, M. E., 'Hypermobility and Knee Injuries', *Physician and Sportsmedicine* 15(6): pp159–65, 1987

Sullivan, P. D., Markos, P. E. and Minor, M. D., *An Intergrated Approach to Therapeutic Exercise Theory and Clinical Application,* Appleton & Lange, 1981

Taylor, P. M. and Taylor, D. K., *Conquering Athletic Injuries,* Leisure Press (Illinois), 1988

Williams, J. G. P. and Sperryn, P. N., *Sports Medicine,* Arnold, 1976

Zelisko, J. A., Noble, H. B. and Porter, M., 'A Comparison of Men's and Women's Professional Basketball Injuries', *American Journal of Sports Medicine* 10: pp197–299, 1982

PLYOMETRICS AND FLEXIBILITY

Adams, T. M., 'An Investigation of Selected Plyometric Training Exercises on Muscular Leg

Strength and Power', *Track and Field Quarterly Review*, pp36–9, 1983.

Allsen, P. E., *Conditioning and Physical Fitness – Current Answers to Relevant Questions*, Wm. C. Brown (Iowa), 1978

Gambetta, V., 'Plyometrics for Beginners – Basic Considerations', *New Studies in Athletics,* pp61–6, March 1989

Gambetta, V., 'Plyometric Training', *Track and Field Quarterly Review* 78(1): pp58–61, 1978

Hartmann, W., 'Selected Bibliography 13 – Plyometric Training', *New Studies in Athletics*, pp93–102, March 1989

Mann, R., 'Plyometrics', *Track and Field Quarterly Review* 81(4): pp55–7, 1981

Millar, B. P. and Power, S. L. D., 'Developing Power in Athletics', *Track and Field Quarterly Review* 81(4): pp52–4, 1981

Moynihan, P. S., 'Plyometrics: Training and Exercises', *Track and Field Quarterly Review* 83(4): pp52–9, 1983

NSA Round Table, 'Plyometrics', *New Studies in Athletics,* pp21–5, March 1989

Radcliffe, J. C. and Farentinos, R. C., *Plyometrics – Explosive Power Training*, 2nd edn, Human Kinetics (Illinois), 1985

Wilt, F., 'Plyometrics', *Track Technique*, 1982

SPORT SPECIFIC REFERENCES

TEXTS COVERING SEVERAL POPULAR SPORTS

Anderson, B., *Stretching*, Pelham Books, 1980

Alter, M. J., *Science of Stretching*, Human Kinetics (Illinois), 1988

Beaulieu, J. E., *Stretching for all Sports*, The Athletic Press (California), 1980

AMERICAN FOOTBALL

Kroll, W. A., *Physical Conditioning for Winning Football*, Allyn & Bacon (Boston), 1983

Moretz, J. A., Walters, R. and Smith, L., 'Flexibility as a Predictor of Knee Injuries in College Football Players', *Physician and Sportsmedicine* 10(7): pp93–7, 1982

ATHLETICS

Rogers, J. L., 'PNF: A New Way to Improve Flexibility', *Track Technique*, pp2345–7, Winter 1978

Song, T. M. K., 'Effects of Seasonal Training on Anthropometry, Flexibility, Strength and Cardiorespiratory Function on Junior Female Track and Field Athletes', *Journal of Sports Medicine* 23: pp168–77, 1983

Surberg, P. R., 'Flexibility Exercise Reexamined', *Athletic Training* 18: pp37–40, 1983

Sutcliffe, P., 'A Mobility Programme for Pole Vaulters', *Athletics Coach* 18(1): pp20–1, 1984

Tancred, W. R., 'Power Training – A Must For All Athletes' *Athletics Coach* 18(1), 1984

Thomas, H., *The AAA's Runner's Guide*, Willow Books, 1987

BADMINTON
Downey, J. and Brodie, D., *Get Fit for Badminton*, Pelham Books, 1980

BASKETBALL
Jeremiah, M. *Coaching Basketball – Ten Winning Concepts*, John Wiley & Sons (New York), 1979

Taylor, A. W., *The Scientific Aspects of Sports Training*, Charles C. Thomas, 1975

Zelisko, J. A., Noble, H. B. and Porter, M., 'A Comparison of Men's and Women's Professional Basketball Injuries', *American Journal of Sports Medicine* 10: pp197–299, 1982

CYCLING
Burke, E., *Science of Cycling*, Human Kinetics (Illinois), 1986

DIVING
Taylor, A. W., *The Scientific Aspects of Sports Training*, Charles C. Thomas, 1975

GOLF
Jenkins, S. P. R., 'Stretching a Point Correctly' *Golf Illustrated Weekly* (UK), 19 February 1988. (Part 1 of 7-part series on fitness for golf by S. P. R. Jenkins.)

Jenkins, S. P. R. and McNaught-Davis, J. P., *Injuries and Fitness of Elite Golf Professionals*. (1991).

Sunningdale Publications, 1 Hamilton Drive, Sunningdale, Berkshire.

GYMNASTICS
Caine, D. J. and Lindner, K. J., 'Overuse Injuries of Growing Bones: The Young Female Gymnast at Risk?', *Physician and Sportsmedicine* 13(12): pp51–64, 1985

Ciullow, J. V. and Jackson, D. W., 'Pars Interarticularis Stress Reaction, Spondylolysis and Spondylolisthesis in Gymnasts', *Clinics in Sports Medicine* 4(1): pp95–110, 1985

George, G. S., *Biomechanics of Women's Gymnastics*, Prentice-Hall (New Jersey), 1980

Goodway, J., 'Injury in Gymnastics – The Practical Implications', *The Gymnast Magazine*, Technical Supplement, May/June 1988

Goodway, J. D., McNaught-Davis, J. P. and White, J., 'The Distribution of Injuries Among Young Female Gymnasts in Relation to Selected Training and Environmental Factors' from *Children and Exercise XIV* edited by G. Beunen et al., Band 4 Schriftenreihe der Hamburg-Mannheimer-Stiftung fur Informationsmedizin, Enke Verlag, 1989

Kirby, R. L., 'Flexibility and Musculo-skeletal Symptomatology in Female Gymnasts and Age-Matched Controls', *American Journal of Sports Medicine* 9: pp160–4, 1981

Nelson, J. K., Johnson, B. L. and Smith, G. C., 'Physical Characterisitics, Hip Flexibility and Arm

Strength of Female Gymnasts Classified by Intensity Training Across Age', *Journal of Sports Medicine* 23: pp95–101, 1983

Steele, V. A. and White, J. A., 'Injury Amongst Female Gymnasts', proceedings of the Society of Sports Sciences: Sport and Science Conference, Liverpool, 1983

Steele, V. A. and White, J. A., 'Injury Prediction in Female Gymnasts', *British Journal of Sports Medicine* 20: pp31–3

Swallow, T. and Swallow M., 'Preparation: Suppleness', *The Gymnast* 17(5): pp8–9, 1980

Weiss, M., 'The Importance of Flexibility', *International Gymnast* 26(7): p53, 1984

MARTIAL ARTS

Oyama, M., *Essential Karate*, Sterling (New York), 1978

Reay T. and Hobbs, G., *The Judo Manual*, Barrie & Jenkins, 1979

POWER LIFTING

Chang, D. E., Bushbacher, L. P. and Edlich, R. F., 'Limited Joint Mobility in Power Lifters', *American Journal of Sports Medicine* 16(3): pp280–4, 1988

RUGBY LEAGUE

Larder, P., *The Rugby League Coaching Manual*, Heinemann, 1988

SOCCER

Ekstrand, J. and Gillquist, J., 'The Frequency of Muscle Tightness and Injuries in Soccer Players', *American Journal of Sports Medicine* 10(2): pp75–8, 1982

Ekstrand, J., Gillquist, J. and Liljedahl, S-O, 'Prevention of Soccer Injuries – Supervision by Doctor and Physiotherapist', *American Journal of Sports Medicine* 11(3): pp116–20, 1983

Hattori, K. and Ohta, S., 'Ankle Joint Flexibility in College Soccer Players', *Journal of Human Ergol* 15: pp85–9, 1986

Muckle, D. S., *Get Fit for Soccer*, Pelham Books, 1981

Rochcongar, P., Morvan, R., Jan, J., Dassonville, J. and Beillot, J., 'Isokinetic Investigation of Knee Extensors and Knee Flexors in Young French Soccer Players', *International Journal of Sports Medicine* 9: pp448–50, 1988

Sutherland, D. M., *Get Fit for Soccer*, Pelham Books, 1981

Taylor, A. W., *The Scientific Aspects of Sports Training*, Charles C. Thomas, 1975

SQUASH

Taylor, J. K., *Squash*, Pelham Books, 1985

SWIMMING

Counsilman, J. E., *Competitive Swimming Manual for Coaches and Swimmers*, Pelham Books, 1978

Garratt, P., *Flexibility for Swimming*, Kaye & Ward, 1980

Greipp, J. F., 'Swimmer's Shoulder: The

Influence of Flexibility and Weight Training', *Physician and Sportsmedicine* 13(8): pp92–105, 1985

Prichard, B., 'Increasing your Range', *Swimming Technique*, pp7–10, Feb–Apr. 1987

Prichard, B., 'Stretching for Speed', *Swimming Technique*, p32–6, May–July 1987

Wilkie, D. and Juba, K., *The Handbook of Swimming*, Pelham Books, 1986

TABLE TENNIS

Burn, B., *The Science of Table Tennis*, Pelham Books, 1979

TENNIS

Hageman, C. E. and Lehman, R. C., 'Stretching, Strengthening and Conditioning for the Competitive Tennis Player', *Clinics in Sports Medicine* 7(2), 1988

Kibler, W. B., Henny, C. C. and McQueen, C., 'Evaluation of Fitness Levels and Injury Patterns in Elite Junior Tennis Players', *Medicine and Science in Sport and Exercises* 18(S24), 1986

VOLLEYBALL

Owolabi, E. O., 'Trunk Flexibility and Vertical Jump Test Scored in Different Units, and Male Volleyball Ability in Nigerian Players', *Scottish Journal of Physical Education* 14(1): pp43–7, 1986

INDEX